Land, Sea, and Sky

LAND, SEA, and SKY

*an introduction to the
wonders of natural science*

by GEORGE GROH

COLLIER BOOKS · *NEW YORK*
COLLIER-MACMILLAN LTD. · *LONDON*

Library of Congress Catalog Card Number: 65-23075

FIRST EDITION 1966

The Macmillan Company, New York

Collier-Macmillan Ltd., Toronto, Ontario

Printed in the United States of America

Contents

I : *The Land*

THE EARTH BENEATH us seems solid and dependable, a well-anchored platform. We know, however, that this is an illusion. Actually, our planet is wheeling in a great orbit through space, spinning as it goes, and reacting continually to the strain of powerful forces within itself. Every now and then such movements and forces make themselves felt in dramatic events.

Consider, for instance, how the earth tilts on its axis. That affects the angle of sunlight, causing glaciers to form at the poles, where the light is least direct and provides little warmth. In times past, some slight change in the balance of forces caused the glaciers to move down from the north, carving fantastic new patterns across the face of the land.

Or consider the hot liquids and gases trapped in the earth layers deep under our feet. The pressures created when these elements combine may build gradually for thousands of years and then erupt in an instant—thrusting up mountains or tearing them apart, spewing out sheets of flaming lava.

Other forces sculpture the land with slow and quiet strokes. The wind for example. Wind carries moisture away from one area and releases it over another; it is a factor in creating in the same latitudes the barren Sahara Desert and the lush green Caribbean islands.

Such is our earth. It is like a living thing, full of restless power, constantly changing in ways we are just beginning to understand.

Glaciers: The Ancient Ice Age

Glaciers are immense masses of ice that cover nearly six million square miles of the earth's surface. They appear in the Arctic and Antarctic and in mountain ranges such as the Rockies, Alps, and Himalayas. In ages past, they spread over still vaster areas, holding more than a fourth of the world in their frozen grip.

Four times in the last million years the glaciers have come crunching down from the north. They pushed deep into Europe, reaching France and Germany, and cut huge swaths through Canada and the United States. In this country, the

The front of Wilson-Piedmont Glacier at Marble Point in the Antarctic. The dark area at the bottom represents accumulation bands of dirt and rock mixed with the ice; the lighter area above is comparatively clean ice. Icicles are caused by melting of the surface snow.

march of the ice mountains advanced at times as far south as present-day Kansas City, Missouri, and Louisville, Kentucky.

The glaciers were set in motion by changes in climate. It is thought that heavy Arctic snows piled up for centuries, forming drifts many thousands of feet deep. Gradually, the drifts pressed themselves into mountains of ice. And then, slowly, the ice mountains began to move. Sliding along under the pressure of their own immense weight, the glaciers rumbled across the land.

The last glacial era was one of the milder ones—and yet it lasted for an estimated 50,000 to 100,000 years. It left great scars on the face of the earth.

In places the glaciers actually warped the earth's crust, the ground sometimes sinking hundreds of feet under the weight of an ice sheet two miles thick. That amounts to a load of nine billion tons per square mile. Hudson Bay and the Great Lakes were probably formed by such earth-squeezing pressure.

In New England the glaciers acted like giant bulldozers, scraping the ground down to bedrock, gouging deep valleys, and piling up jumbled hills. In the process, enormous quantities of earth were scooped up, carried along, and finally dumped out at points where the glaciers melted. Places like Cape Cod and Long Island came into being as glacial dump piles.

Other glacial action carved the scenic countryside of Minnesota and Wisconsin. One small glacial scar near Two Creeks, Wisconsin, is especially interesting because it marks the southernmost edge of the last ice sheet. When the glacier there gave its final lurch, it plowed through a spruce forest, snapping off the tree trunks as though they were matchsticks. Radiocarbon studies of the long-buried tree remains indicate that it happened about 11,000 years ago.

The glaciers changed the nature of life all over the country. Herds of woolly mammoths roamed through the frozen wasteland that was New England. Moose grazed on the New Jersey tundra, within sight of the looming ice cliffs. Musk-oxen appeared as far south as Texas, and walrus swam among floating ice cakes off the coast of Georgia.

The greatest change of all was the appearance of man in the New World. That, too, was probably a result of the Ice Age. The theory is that primitive people somehow crossed the Bering Strait and spread down through America after glaciers drove them out of their Siberian hunting grounds. They may have traveled just ahead of an advancing ice sheet, or they may have found their way through gaps in the glaciers. In any case, they made it, and so became the first immigrants to the New World. They were the ancestors of the American Indians.

The glacial era was brought to an end by another shift in the world's climate. For some still-mysterious reason, the summers became a little longer and warmer, the winters a little less cold, and the ice began to melt away. Most of the melting took place at the southern edge of the ice pack, and so it appeared that the glaciers were retreating, going back to the place from which they had come.

The retreat was often very gradual. In the Connecticut Valley, for instance, it took 22 years for one mile of glacier to disappear. But when such melting continued year after year across the whole width of the continent, it released astonishing amounts of water. In time the world sea level rose as much as 400 feet. And that brought the threat of flood to many lands.

The legend and literature of very early civilizations tell of some terrible floods during this period. The story of Noah's Ark is one familiar example. Ancient India had a similar story of a flood so disastrous that many thought it marked the end of the world. Then, too, there is the tale of Atlantis, the "lost kingdom," supposedly engulfed by the sea. Such stories may record man's dim recollections of a time when grinding ice mountains became transformed into swollen seas.

Today the glaciers are safely tucked away in their polar homelands, but there is no reason to believe that they will remain locked up there forever. They may melt even more, creating new floods. Or they may come rumbling down again. Some scientists believe that a new glacial era may begin within the next thousand years.

The Poles: The Living Ice Age

The North and South Poles have been described as the "living Ice Age." At these end points, the globe is still covered by thick slabs of ice that may well have formed thousands of centuries ago.

The South Pole has the dubious distinction of being the colder and bleaker, the temperature in its vicinity sometimes falling as low as −80 degrees Fahrenheit. It is guarded, moreover, by glaciers so massive and so grimly forbidding that for a long time they concealed one of the great physical facts of our planet. The South Pole is in Antarctica, a continent almost as big as South America, and yet this huge landmass was not discovered until a little more than a century ago.

The North Pole is situated in the Arctic Ocean and is covered by a sheet of ice several hundred feet thick. The temperature sometimes goes down to about −60 degrees Fahrenheit, the lowest readings being recorded at a Siberian spot not far from the pole.

The Arctic warms a little in summer—even the pole enjoys an occasional summer day above freezing—but it still is a harsh and cruel region. Some idea of the conditions can perhaps best be gained by taking an imaginary walking tour. If one were to start at the North Pole and walk down the face of North America, advancing 20 miles a day, one would struggle for 14 weeks over ice packs and frozen tundra before seeing the first tree. To put it another way, the distance between the North Pole and the nearest tree is greater than the distance between Minnesota and Mexico.

The great weight of polar ice masses is thought to influence the tilt of the planet and to affect the way that earth wobbles as it spins in its axis. This in turn may have far-reaching effects on world climate and on the behavior of the poles themselves. In investigating such possibilities, some scientists have come to the astonishing conclusion that the poles may be wandering about on the face of the earth.

To follow the theory, one must understand the clues that scientists utilize in uncovering earth's history. The growth rings of trees, for instance, provide a very important clue. It is known that trees in temperate zones grow in seasonal spurts, developing well-marked growth rings as a record of

The fossil remains of a mulberry leaf (*Morus symmetrica*) sealed in shale formed by lava deposits almost a million years ago.

Courtesy of the American Museum of Natural History

each annual cycle. Tropical trees, on the other hand, grow steadily and continuously, leaving no rings. Fortunately, these trees are sometimes buried in earth under conditions that produce coal, and the coal often retains a print of the material that formed it, even down to the shape of a leaf or the pattern of a tree ring. Thus, by examining coal, we can obtain very good estimates of climate conditions hundreds of millions of years ago.

Another valuable clue comes from the little corals that thrive in warm salt water. Their remains help us to trace the ebb and flow of ancient seas and provide another indication as to temperatures in ages past.

And then there is the clue of "fossil winds." Here we start with the fact that winds blow in certain well-defined patterns, which are partly determined by heat and cold. In regions like the equator, long-continued prevailing winds leave their mark on the land by sorting dust and sand into dunes of particular shapes. In some instances, the dunes retain their shape while changing into sandstone, preserving a fossil record of ancient wind directions.

Such evidence is all circumstantial, but when added up it offers fascinating paradoxes. In the cases cited above, it adds up to deposits of jungle coal in the Arctic, coral remains off the chilly coast of Korea, and a fossil wind that could indicate that the equator once passed through Wisconsin on a line running north and south rather than east and west. It has led some scientists to the radical theory that 400 million years ago the North Pole was located in the mid-Pacific, migrating from there to Guam and Japan and on across Siberia to its present location. The South Pole meantime was supposedly engaged in a similar trek across Africa. The theory is by no means established, but if it should be correct it would go far toward explaining the dramatic climate changes that have occurred time and again in earth's history.

Sahara: The Largest Desert

In Arabic, the word from which the name Sahara is derived means "the desert." It is a fitting name for this dry, barren, almost lifeless wasteland.

The Sahara is the world's largest desert, sprawling over about three and a half million square miles. Its boundaries extend from the Atlantic shore of Africa to the Nile and from the Mediterranean to the Sudan. It is a region almost as large as Europe.

We think of the Sahara as a land where scorching sun beats down on endless sand dunes. True, the dunes cover more than half a million square miles. The Sahara's distinctive characteristic, however, is not the sand, or even the heat, but the lack of water. The average annual rainfall over the whole region is less than four inches a year.

One of the most forbidding spots is Tanezrouft, in the Algerian Sahara. It contains neither a blade of grass nor an insect. The noonday temperature often registers 125 degrees Fahrenheit, and the surface heat of the sand rises to more than 150 degrees Fahrenheit. A man lost in Tanezrouft would not survive a day.

Surprisingly, there are other areas where the Sahara becomes a cold desert, sometimes freezing cold. In the Ahaggar Mountain region of the central Sahara, the temperature plummets as much as 40 degrees in an hour when the sun goes down. The mountain section obtains a little moisture from snowcapped peaks, but even here the dryness is pervasive; some places along the Ahaggar range have recorded seven straight years without rain.

Still other areas consist of immense salt beds laid down by prehistoric seas. In such Sahara villages as Agorgott and Smeida, the natives live in huts carved from salt blocks.

Generally, the Sahara's terrain consists of sand, rock, or

parched earth, relieved here and there by oases, where life-giving water flows from deep underground springs. Some oases spread out for 20 or 30 square miles, supporting populations as high as 50,000 people.

Some of Sahara's inhabitants prefer a hard life in the open desert to settled existence around an oasis. This is especially true of the colorful Berbers, who roam the country with flocks of camels, goats, and sheep. The Berbers have long been famed as warriors, hunters, and superb riders; their knowledge of the desert enables them to exist where others could not.

Berber boys are brought up in a stern code; they are taught to withstand heat, thirst, hunger, and pain, learning to pride themselves on the toughness of their lean, hard bodies. Among Berber girls, however, the mark of prestige and position takes a very different form. A chief's daughter is encouraged to gorge and grow fat; some are known to consume a dozen quarts of goat's milk a day and weigh as much as 300 pounds! The reason is not hard to understand. In a country where most people must struggle for food, fatness is visible proof of wealth and position.

The Amazon: The Most Powerful River

More than 400 years ago, the Spanish adventurer Francisco de Orellana explored an immense river in South America, following it from its headwaters high in the Andes Mountains to its mouth on the Atlantic shore of Brazil. When he returned to civilization, he told amazing tales of what he had seen. He said that the country along the river was ruled by a tribe of savage white women who were taller, stronger, and fiercer than any men. These warrior women went nearly naked, De Orellana said, and yet they lived in splendid cities and wore exquisite ornaments of silver and gold.

De Orellana's account resembled an old Greek legend about warrior women who were called Amazons. Thus it was that the river became known as the Amazon.

The story of the Amazonian superwomen was just an adventurer's tall tale, and one wonders why De Orellana bothered to make it up. He was the first explorer to travel the entire length of the most spectacular river in the world, and the things he actually had seen were far more remarkable than any legend.

Along its 3,900-mile length, the Amazon is fed by more than a thousand tributaries, ten of them larger than the Rhine. When it is swollen by tropical rains, it rises 60 feet, flooding an area larger than Poland. At its mouth is an island that is larger than Switzerland. It is 200 miles wide at the mouth, and it empties into the sea at a rate of up to almost three and a half billion gallons a minute, twelve times the flow of the Mississippi. Its surging, silt-laden current is so powerful that it continues to form a clearly marked channel for more than a hundred miles after it enters the ocean.

It is not quite the longest river—the Nile is 245 miles longer —but no river on earth compares with the Amazon in total size and power. It is so broad and deep that ships can navigate it for distances greater than the voyage from New York to Ireland.

The Amazon's immense basin contains one-fourth of the world's forest land. It is lush, thick-growing jungle, swarming with wildlife, but very sparsely inhabited by man. Much of it has never been explored.

The country offers obstacles and dangers enough to discourage all but the hardiest explorers. The river is home to huge crocodiles and to tiny but fierce man-eating fish called piranhas. Jaguars slink through the surrounding jungle, and 40-foot snakes called anacondas lie in wait along the paths. An anaconda can crush a calf in its coils, then consume the

United Press International Photo

Natives of the Jivaro tribe display the shrunken head of a victim.

animal in a single meal; it is one of the few reptiles that deliberately attack man.

Amazon Indians include some of the most savage of primitive peoples. Most of them fight with poisoned arrows, and some are headhunters. The Jivaro tribesmen employ a secret formula that enables them to shrink a human head to the size of an orange. In the strange code of the jungle, the Jivaro think they are conferring great honor on a man when they shrink his head. They do it only to enemies whom they especially admire, believing that the rite transfers the victim's strong qualities to themselves.

A still greater danger to Amazon explorers is the silent, invisible menace of jungle disease. Malaria, leprosy, and yellow fever are some of the common scourges. In much of the region, the average lifetime of the natives is only 30 to 40 years. Today, however, medical science is conquering the ills,

bringing nearer the day when the wild Amazon country will
be opened up by a surge of pioneers.

Everest: The Tallest Mountain

Towering high over the Himalayas is the lordly peak of
Mount Everest, the tallest mountain in the world. It rises
29,028 feet, or more than five and a half miles.

The summit is as barren and rugged a spot as exists anywhere on earth. Icy winds of 150 miles an hour shriek around
the pinnacle, giving a savage bite to temperatures that hover
at −50 degrees Fahrenheit. Nothing grows at the top; nothing
moves or stirs except the wind-whipped snow; no wild creature ever approaches this harsh aerie on the roof of the world.

Only man finds in such a place an irresistible challenge.

The lure that Everest has for adventurers was expressed by
George Leigh-Mallory, one of the first to attempt the climb.
He said that he would pit himself against this biggest mountain "because it is there." For Leigh-Mallory, it was a challenge that cost his life. When he was last seen he was clawing
his way up a mist-shrouded slope only 800 feet from the
top. He may have made it, but he never returned, and his
body was never found. For forty years he has lain buried
somewhere under Everest's mantle of everlasting snow.

Fourteen other expeditions have tried it, at least ten of them
failing. Some of the climbers fell to their death from the steep
slopes or were swept off by avalanches; some tumbled into
deep ice canyons concealed by crusts of covering snow. Many
were turned back by cold, exhaustion, lack of food, even lack
of air. On Everest's upper reaches, oxygen is so rare that mere
breathing requires a supreme effort. But the climbers kept
trying. Finally, in 1953, there came the triumphant moment
when Sir Edmund Hillary and a Sherpa guide, Tensing Nor-
kay, stood together on the lonely summit, where no man had
set foot before.

The years since have been marked by a steady parade of climbers to the top. A Swiss team accomplished it in 1956, and a Soviet-Chinese team reported reaching the peak in 1960. Then, recently, two American teams achieved a double conquest, scaling the slope by different routes and arriving at the top on the same day.

The recent conquests all underline the swift crumbling of physical frontiers in this adventurous age.

Krakatoa: Violent Volcano

The most violent explosion in modern history occurred not from an H-bomb but from the forces of nature. It was the eruption of Krakatoa, a volcanic island near Java, in 1883.

The eruption ripped the top off the mountainous island, hurling a cubic mile of dirt and rocks 20 miles into the sky. The mass of material hurled into space was equal to four times the weight of all the great buildings on New York's Manhattan Island. From the huge hole thus created, there poured forth such a stream of boiling lava that whole new islands were formed.

The mighty convulsion gave rise to a tidal wave—a wall of water 115 feet high—that surged across the ocean at 100 miles an hour. The wave's effect was felt in the English Channel, half a world away. The sound blast from the eruption traveled seven times around the world, each passage being recorded by scientific instruments in London and Berlin. The roar was heard clearly for 2,500 miles. For two years afterward, dust and ash from Krakatoa swirled through the stratosphere, creating strangely beautiful red-and-gold sunsets over much of the globe.

No one on the island survived the explosion, and more than 35,000 people were drowned in the tidal wave that followed the blast.

Krakatoa is quiet now, but there are 500 other active

volcanoes in various parts of the world that sputter ominously and sometimes burst forth in flames. The cause of such eruptions is still not thoroughly understood. Some scientists believe that the earth's interior is a mass of fiery gases and molten lava and that volcanoes occur when the lava boils out through fissures in the earth's thin top layer, or crust. Others say that the inner layers are solid rock, with shifting earth pressures occasionally creating such intense heat that the rock melts and becomes lava.

Whatever the reasons, volcanoes have been erupting through the ages. Indeed, many of the great mountain ranges were created in volcanic upheavals of unimaginable force. There was, for instance, one series of explosions that deposited a foot-deep layer of white ash along most of South America's Pacific shore. It happened in prehistoric times, about 68,000 years ago, when the entire spine of the Andes was torn by stupendous eruptions. The whole earth must have shuddered then with explosions even more awesome than that of Krakatoa.

White-hot lava bubbles from the crater of an active volcano on the island of Fayal in the Azores.

International News Photo

II: *The Sea*

THE SEA EXTENDS over nearly three-fourths of the globe. It would cover the entire globe were it not that the earth's warped and buckled crust thrusts some areas up out of reach. On a perfectly smooth earth, the water everywhere would stand two miles deep.

It appears almost certain that millions of years ago the sea gave birth to the first forms of life. Now it nourishes life. It gives up 80,000 cubic miles of water in the form of evaporation every year and then regains the water after the world has been washed with rain.

The surface of the sea is churned constantly by tides and powerful currents. In the sea's depths is a mysterious mountain range, the biggest in the world; its presence lends support to an almost unbelievable theory about the planet's history.

Much more may lie hidden beneath the waves, for the ocean depths, which have been called our inner space, are still far from explored. It has been said that we know less about the sea than we do about the far-off moon.

Sargasso: Strange Jungle on the Water

One of the world's largest jungles is found not on land but on water. It is the Sargasso Sea, a weed-choked region of the mid-Atlantic that extends over about 23,000 square miles. It stretches from Bermuda to the Antilles and from mid-ocean to a point near the Florida coast, covering in all an area as large as Holland and Belgium combined.

Christopher Columbus was the first to see and report on this strange region. When he sailed into the Sargasso Sea on his first voyage to the New World, he was certain that he was approaching land. It was a reasonable belief, since mariners had never before observed weed growths except in places near the shore. As Columbus sailed on and on, however, it became clear that this was something new and different. His sailors grew fearful, thinking that there was something odd and dangerous about lush plants in the midst of an ocean. They were deathly afraid of being trapped in the weed-filled waters that stretched as far as the eye could see. Ever since then, marine legends have pictured the Sargasso Sea as a graveyard of lost ships.

The truth is more interesting than the legends. This marine jungle is not dangerous at all, but it is a very special place, containing forms of life quite different from those found anywhere else on the planet.

To begin with, it is an area of relatively calm water in an ocean otherwise noted for the constant movement of its currents. It is, in fact, a kind of giant pool in the restless sea. Its boundaries are formed by the Gulf Stream, the equatorial currents, and the Antilles Islands.

Life in the Sargasso Sea has taken peculiar shapes because of the unusual conditions. Everywhere else, for instance, seaweed crumbles and sinks to the bottom when it is torn loose from its moorings in shallow water. But in the Sargasso Sea a different kind of seaweed has developed. It floats on the surface, puts out new crops by splitting in two, and grows in a "sea soil" produced by the floating remains of its own kind.

The fish life is different, too. Twelve distinct species of fish, snails, shrimps, crustaceans, and worms are found in the Sargasso Sea that are not known to exist anywhere else. One of the odd ones is a species called the sargassum fish. It fits perfectly into its environment, its golden-brown, frond-like fins making it look exactly like a clump of seaweed. It feeds off the small crustaceans that flourish in this area, and it makes use of the weeds as a nest for its eggs.

The Sargasso Sea swarms also with sea horses, the curious little fishes that look like knights in a chess set. Sea horses can be found in most warm, weedy marine waters, but they are most abundant in Sargasso. They are notable for an unusual breeding arrangement, the female laying the eggs in a pouch of the male. When the young hatch, they remain in the pouch for a time, receiving their nourishment by attaching themselves to their father's blood vessels. When the proper time comes, the father performs a "dance" of birth, twisting and turning as he tears his offspring loose from his body and spins them out of the pouch.

The sargassum fish so closely resembles a clump of seaweed that it is difficult to distinguish from its surroundings.

United Press International Photo

Perhaps the most curious of all Sargasso's creatures are the seagoing eels that return to this region of their birth to breed and die. Drawn by some mysterious urge, they migrate from Europe and America, in some cases traveling 2,000 miles to reach this one special place in the ocean. When they arrive at Sargasso, they dive deep into the abyss; there they mate, lay their eggs, and end their lives.

The young live for several years in Sargasso's protected waters. Then the mysterious migration urge appears again in another form. The young eels leave the Sargasso Sea, swim into the Gulf Stream, and begin the long trip to the home of their ancestors. At a certain point in the journey, some of them veer off to American waters, while others are carried into the seas bordering Europe.

The curious thing is that the eels have never been known to make a mistake. The American and European eels are quite different, and in each case the young always seem to return with unerring instinct to the home waters of their parents.

What guides these migrations? Why do the parent eels always come to this particular region to breed? How do the young find their way to homes they have never seen? Marine scientists have been puzzled and fascinated by such questions for years and have not found an answer yet. It remains one of the riddles of the Sargasso Sea.

The Gulf Stream: Great River in the Atlantic

More than 450 years ago, the explorer Juan Ponce de León stood on the deck of his ship watching the sails and scarcely believing what he saw. A strong wind was whipping in from the stern, filling the sails, and yet his ship was scudding not forward but backward. He was being swept off his course by the powerful, swift-moving current of the Gulf Stream.

Ponce de León encountered the Gulf Stream off the coast

of Florida and was the first explorer to report it. For a long time afterward, however, many mariners remained ignorant of its existence. Indeed, as late as 1770, British seamen still did not list it on their navigation charts. The British learned of it finally when they asked Benjamin Franklin to explain why some routes to America always proved much quicker than others. Franklin did not know, but he sought an answer from wise old Yankee whalers. They were well acquainted with the Gulf Stream. They had no charts of it; they just knew from long experience where to catch it for a fast ride and how to avoid it when they were going in the opposite direction. Later, Franklin himself prepared the first chart of the Gulf Stream, dropping marked bottles along the coast in order to compute the speed and direction of flow.

Today the Gulf Stream is known to be a main artery in a system of streams that pulse through the Atlantic. There are at least four streams in the system, but they are so closely related that they may be considered as forming one great river in the sea. It follows a circular path, beginning as an equatorial current that sweeps west from Africa, becoming the Gulf Stream as it swirls through the Caribbean and flows up the American coast. At Labrador it turns east and loops back through the North Atlantic, sending off eddies and side currents that wash the shores of Europe.

Tremendous amounts of water are caught up in the Gulf Stream. In places it is a mile deep and a hundred miles wide. It flows at a rate of up to five miles an hour, transporting as much as 100 billion tons of water an hour. In short, it is a marine river a thousand times as big as the mighty Mississippi.

The Gulf Stream's water is generally 20 degrees warmer than that of the surrounding ocean. It gathers heat as it swings through the southern loop of its course, then slowly releases its warmth as it courses north. It is thought that warmth released by the Gulf Stream affects the entire climate

of Northern Europe, making green lands of places like England and Ireland, which would otherwise be snowbound and
desolate.

The Gulf Stream also has an enormous effect on life in the
sea. It plows across the ocean floor, stirring up foodstuff for
the fishes and creating conditions favorable to thick-
swarming marine life of every kind. It is estimated that the
creatures of the Gulf Stream are more numerous and more
varied than all the species of animal life found on land.

Fundy: The World's Highest Tides

Twice each day the great pulse of the ocean sends some 3,680
billion cubic feet of water surging into Nova Scotia's Bay of
Fundy. The water pours through the bay's wide mouth,
then piles up 40 to 50 feet high as it funnels into narrow
converging channels. It is the highest tide on earth.

This immense movement of water seems surprisingly
gentle when seen from the shore. At low tide one can look
out over the bay and see mile on mile of red-brown mud
flats sloping down to the sea. Then the tide rolls in, and the
mud flats disappear under tons of water. It happens so
quietly and on so large a scale that the speed with which it
occurs is not really apparent. People who live near the Bay
of Fundy, however, are not deceived. When they venture
out on the flats, they keep a wary eye on the ocean, knowing
that if they start back too late the water will overtake them.
Once, a woman was caught and pulled under while gallop-
ing across the flats on a horse.

People who live in the area take advantage of the tide by
using a curious method of fishing. They string nets in the air,
hanging them from the tops of tall poles at the outer edge
of the flats. The tide washes in, buries a net under many
feet of water, then recedes, leaving sturgeon and sea bass
flopping about in what has once more become an aerial net.

The ebb and flow of the tide are even more dramatically illustrated at little Walton Harbor in an upper region of the bay. At high tide, freight ships float alongside the loading wharves; but at low tide, the same ships lie beached on the mud flats like stranded whales. They must be tied to the wharves with strong cables to keep them from rolling over into the mud.

Effects of the tide can be seen also at places where the incoming sea surges up the mouth of a river. The result is called a tidal bore. At Fundy's Petitcodiac River, the tidal bore creates a foaming, churning wall of water five feet high that rushes upriver as fast as a man can run. The sound of its passing is like that of an express train at full throttle.

Fundy's tides are created, of course, by the pull of sun and moon on ocean waters. But that is not the whole explanation, as can be seen by visiting Nantucket Island, only a few hundred miles south of Nova Scotia. Here the same planetary forces tug at the same Atlantic waters, creating a tiny, scarcely noticeable tide only one foot high.

The reasons for such differences are complicated, but the chief factor is not difficult to understand. As the earth spins through the heavens, the oceans splash back and forth like water rocked in a bucket. This splashing motion has a regular rhythm, but one that varies from place to place according to the size and shape of a particular ocean basin. In some places, such as Fundy, huge tides occur because the upward surge of the splash comes as the same time that the sun and moon exert their tidal pull. At places such as Nantucket, the splashing motion runs opposite to the tidal pull; one force counteracts the other, holding the tide to a mere ripple.

Whether large or small, the tides clearly indicate the considerable influence that cosmic forces exert on our planet. Tidal movement churns the oceans, shapes the shore, and affects even the motion of the earth itself. Scientists believe

that over millions of years, tidal friction has slowed the
speed at which the earth spins on its axis, gradually changing
the rotation rate from once every 4 hours to once every 24.
It is thought that the process will go on until the earth
rotates only once a month. Then, billions of years from now,
the pull and haul of cosmic forces will be in balance, and
the tides will be still.

The Mid-Atlantic Ridge: Mountains in the Sea

Rising from the floor of the Atlantic Ocean is a massive
mountain range called the Mid-Atlantic Ridge. It is the
world's largest mountain system; but more than that, it offers
a fascinating clue to the possible shape of earth in a far-
distant past.

The range has a few visible landmarks, thrusting high
peaks above the waves to form islands such as Ascension,
St. Paul Rocks, and the Azores. Most of it, however, lies
buried deep in the sea. The range begins near Iceland, runs
down the center of the Atlantic to a point below Africa, then
swings to the east. It is about 10,000 miles long and some
500 miles wide.

To oceanographers the shape of the ridge is even more
intriguing than its size, for this submarine mountain range
twists and turns in a very peculiar fashion, duplicating almost
exactly the shape of the continental shorelines on either side.

The odd boundary pattern is one of two facts that lend
support to a remarkable theory. The other fact involves the
shape of the landmasses themselves. It is a point best appre-
ciated by looking at a map. Observe the two hemispheres
as they face each other across the Atlantic, then imagine
that you are pushing the landmasses together. With a little
squeezing they would seem to fit almost as neatly as pieces
in a jigsaw puzzle. Thus the hook of Scandinavia drops into

Ascension Island is one of the few visible landmarks of the massive mountain range called the Mid-Atlantic Ridge.

Hudson Bay, the curving coastline of Spain and France closes around Labrador, the bulge of Africa nestles into the Caribbean. Moreover, if the Mid-Atlantic Ridge were raised up and shown on the map, the evidence would be still more dramatic; it looks for all the world like a strip torn from the middle of the puzzle.

Such are the clues. The staggering theory is that the two hemispheres were at one time solidly joined. Scientists suggest that a colossal upheaval ripped the landmass in two and that the pieces slowly drifted apart, leaving the Mid-Atlantic Ridge as a jagged splinter marking the line of cleavage.

If such a cataclysm took place, it must have occurred when earth's crust rested on a very soft, spongy, almost fluid base. Some scientists add that even today the base may be more fluid than we suppose; they believe the two landmasses may still be drifting apart at an infinitesimal rate of about one foot every thousand years.

Whether the drift theory is correct or not, there is definite evidence that some decidedly earthshaking events have taken place along the Mid-Atlantic Ridge. Oceanographers have located a gigantic rift, or earth fracture, that runs all along the center of the ridge. Earthquake shocks often originate in this fracture, indicating some ancient earth injury that has not yet healed.

Guyots: Mystery of the Flat Tops

During World War II, naval vessels coursed back and forth in the Pacific using sound-detection gear to search for submarines. Occasionally the sound echoes that bounced back revealed a sudden dramatic change in the depth of the water. Later, marine explorers found the explanation. The Pacific is studded with strange, flat-topped mountains, which are known now as guyots.

Undersea mountains are common enough; it was their flat tops that aroused the curiosity of oceanographers. The guyots appeared to be extinct volcanoes and so should have been cone-shaped. The peaks could not have been washed away by the sea, because in the quiet, slow-moving water of the great depths there is almost no erosion. As scientists puzzled over it, they arrived at two possible solutions.

The guyots may be the world's oldest mountains, formed before the sea existed. They may have towered over a bare, empty world a billion years ago, and their tops may have been smoothed away by countless eons of wind before the sea finally rose to engulf them.

Then again, they may have been not the oldest mountains but the biggest. Some scientists believe that the tops eroded away at a time when their massive peaks rose high above sea level. According to this theory, the guyots were so heavy that over the ages they sank into the sea floor, leaving only the stubs that remain today.

These guyots are interesting not only in terms of the questions they raise concerning their origin but in what they suggest about the unexplored domain below the waves. Only a generation ago, the existence of these mountains was not even suspected; yet today we know that more than 500 of them exist. If the sea can conceal so many mountains for so long, then who can guess what other wonders lie still undiscovered in the depths?

The Great Barrier Reef: Fantastic Coral Colonies

Extending for some 1,250 miles along Australia's northeastern coast is the world's largest coral reef. It is an awesome rock formation built from the stony skeletons of tiny creatures.

Courtesy of the American Museum of Natural History

Coral reefs swarm with a variety of marine life. A squirrelfish swims above *Orbicella* coral, while a bear crab (*Scyllarus*) lurks at the base of a triple head of double-ridged brain coral (*Diploria cerebriformis*).

The reef-building creatures are marine animals called coral polyps. When they are born, they wriggle about for a time in shallow water, then anchor themselves and begin to form the limestone shells in which they live. Whole colonies cluster on top of one another, the colonies taking such shapes as stars, lacy fans, and delicate spires. One type is called the staghorn coral because a cluster resembles a pair of antlers. Another type, the organ coral, builds row on row of long, hollow tubes that do indeed look like organ pipes.

Coral colors are as spectacular as their shapes. The creatures are red, green, purple, blue—every shade of the rainbow. Whole sections of the reef sometimes change color as sun and sea create changing conditions of light and shadow.

By day most corals nestle in their shells. At night, on the high tide, the shells open and the corals spread forth poisonous tentacles. Thus they catch and kill worms, larvae, and tiny fish washed in by the waves. It is in holding out these deadly tentacles that corals take on their most graceful shape and dazzling color.

Growing among the corals are curious pink-tinted marine plants called algae. They, too, are encrusted in a stony, limestone-like covering of their own secretion. Some of the algae are as fragile as glass, and yet they are the real cement of the reef, holding it together against the destructive forces of wind and water.

The sea hammers constantly at the reef, carving caves and grottoes below the waterline, pounding the surface rock and shell into brittle sand. In some places, great chunks have been whittled off to form coral islands. But the reef continually rebuilds itself as countless billions of coral and algae lay down fresh deposits of stony remains. It is estimated that the little plants and animals create a new layer of reef at a rate of one foot every 300 years.

The reef swarms with many kinds of marine species. Often

they are brilliantly colored to match their surroundings. Some are dangerous to man. All live in ways peculiar to this special world of barren, rocky ridge and crashing surf.

Every night, soldier crabs appear by the thousands, emerging from beaches laid bare by ebb tide. They march up and down the reef shore, maneuvering like army battalions as they forage for food. At dawn they disappear, scuttling back to the waterline and burying themselves in the sand in order to hide from their enemies, the birds.

Shallow waters along the reef provide a hiding place for giant clams. Some of them measure as much as four feet across and weigh up to 600 pounds. Their shells are of drab gray, but when they open their great mouth-like valves they reveal satiny inner tissues of brilliant green. The clams are blind, yet they have organs in their bodies that react instantly to light. When the flitting shadow of a fish passes above them, they pop their great jaws shut with such force that a jet of water shoots up three feet or more in the air above. A man caught by such a clam might easily suffer a broken arm or leg and be held fast until he drowned.

In the same waters can be found the clam's small relative, the cone-shell mollusk. It is about four inches long and is so gorgeously patterned that collectors consider the shell a prize item. But it, too, is dangerous. It is armed with a barbed, poison-tipped stiletto that flashes out when it is disturbed.

More deadly still is the stonefish, which carries a row of 13 needle-sharp venomous spears along its back. It is an exceedingly ugly thing, gnarled, wrinkled, and warted so as to resemble dead coral or crumbling, weather-beaten rock. It lurks motionless on the sandy bottom and bristles its spears to impale intruders.

The reef's bright little clown fish has no weapon but borrows a neighbor's to protect itself. When pursued, it seeks safety by darting into the thick green shrubbery of the sea

The green seagoing turtle makes its way across the beach to a point above the waterline to lay its eggs.

United Press International Photo

anemone's poisonous tentacles. No one knows why it alone is immune to the anemone's paralyzing touch. The clown fish is well named for its coloration—its orange-red body is overlaid with exaggerated white stripes that look as though they were painted on for comic effect.

Also aptly named is the parrot fish, a pink-and-green creature with a hard, bony, parrot-like beak. Its jaws are powerful enough to crush rock, but it is quite harmless. It actually lives off the reef, munching away at the coral in order to get at the algae embedded in the rock.

Other forms of life come from great distances to use the reef as a breeding ground. The most spectacular of these annual visitors are the Antarctic sperm whales, which migrate some 6,000 miles in order to calve in the warm, protected lagoon that lies between the reef and the Australian mainland.

Huge green seagoing turtles employ the reef shore as a hatchery. At egg-laying time the mother turtle comes out of the sea and plods up the beach in an absolutely straight line, climbing painfully and clumsily over any jagged rocks that lie in the way. She will not alter her route a foot to the right or left to find an easier path. At a point well above the waterline, she scoops a deep hole and lays about a hundred eggs, each about the size of a ping-pong ball. She covers them with sand to provide warmth and protection, then waddles away. Several weeks later the young hatch, dig themselves out, and head straight for the water, moving quickly in an effort to reach the sea before the wheeling birds that feed on them can descend.

The birds themselves are the most numerous of the seasonal visitors that come to breed. Noddy terns, sooty terns, boobies, and muttonbirds all flock in from the South Seas for that purpose. They make a noisy business of it, filling the air with their wild cries. In times long past, ships steered clear of the nesting region because superstitious sailors heard the cries and thought the place was haunted by lost souls.

The Great Barrier Reef today is still an area little known to man. A few sentinels keep watch at lonely lighthouse stations. A few scientists come and go, studying the teeming, colorful aquatic life. Lately, the place has been visited also by adventurous skin divers, who prowl about in the picturesque coral grottoes beneath the waves. Despite all such intruders, however, there remain long, lonely stretches of beach where no human being has ever been known to set foot.

The Marianas Trench: Deepest Hole in the World

About seven miles beneath the rolling waves of the Western Pacific is a huge pit in the ocean floor. It is the Marianas Trench, the deepest hole in the world.

The size of the pit can best be grasped by comparison with another great landmark. If Mount Everest were stood upright in the Marianas Trench, the tip of the mountain would be buried under more than a mile of water.

The ocean floors contain nearly two dozen other trenches that are almost as deep. They are found near volcanic islands

and no doubt were created by the same violent earth spasms
that heaved the islands up from the depths.

The Marianas Trench takes its name from the nearby
Marianas Islands, situated halfway between Wake Island and
the Philippines, in an area where the earth's crust has often
been torn and fractured by interior forces of heat and pressure. Earthquake shocks frequently rumble out of the trench,
setting off tidal waves of devastating power.

The bottom of the trench is one of the most desolate places
on the globe. It is very cold, just a degree or two above
freezing, and darker than the blackest night. No ray of sun
has penetrated there for more than a billion years. There is
another special condition that is hard for us to imagine. The
water at that depth actually squeezes itself with its own
weight, creating pressures powerful enough to shrink a steel
rod. And yet life manages to exist under these conditions.
When scientists went down in a diving machine to explore the
trench, the first thing they saw at the bottom was a foot-long,
flat-bodied fish.

A fish of the deep survives through a kind of pressure-pump
system within its own body. This "pump" produces pressure
at the rate of 10,000 pounds per square inch, enabling the fish
to resist the squeezing force of the sea. As long as the inside
and outside pressures are balanced, the fish is in no danger.
But if such a fish rose to the surface, it would explode, burst-
ing apart from the sudden release of the pent-up force within
itself.

The fishes of the great depths are provided with other
mechanisms well adapted to this environment. Many have
phosphorescent lights to illumine their way through the
eternal night. Some turn on a kind of searchlight when hunting their prey. Others use light as bait, waving glowing
antennae above their gaping jaws. At some levels in the
Marianas Trench, such fish lights shine as bright and as

numerous as stars in the sky. But at other levels, the fishes become scarce and the darkness prevails again.

The exploration of the trench required a very special kind of diving machine. A submarine was out of the question. It is designed for much shallower dives, and it would be crushed like an eggshell by the pressures of the trench. Also discarded was the bathysphere, a diving device that consists of a hollow steel ball at the end of a cable. That could be made strong enough, but there was a danger that the cable would snap, leaving the divers trapped seven miles underwater. A descent into the deepest hole seemed impossible, in fact, until a Swiss scientist named Auguste Piccard came up with a simple but brilliant solution.

Piccard called his device a bathyscaph. He started with the hollow-ball idea, building a steel-walled cabin chamber stout enough to withstand any depth. For windows, he used thick slabs of fused quartz, a material almost as tough as steel. The cabin compartment was only six and a half feet in diameter, yet it was so massively constructed that it weighed more than 11 tons.

Piccard eliminated the danger of a broken cable by not using one. Instead, he attached the cabin to a great steel bag filled with some 30,000 gallons of gasoline. Since gasoline is lighter than water, the bathyscaph floated like a cork. To make it go down, Piccard attached more than 10 tons of iron weights. When he wanted to ascend, he had only to release the weights and the bathyscaph would rise to the surface of its own accord.

Piccard's son, Jacques, finished his father's work by taking the bathyscaph to the bottom of the Marianas Trench in 1960. Sharing in the adventurous dive was Lieutenant Don Walsh of the United States Navy. For nearly five hours, the two men huddled together in the cramped little cabin compartment, all the while gliding down through the dark, silent underwater

The bathyscaphe *Trieste*—designed by Auguste Piccard and his son, Jacques, for research work at great ocean depths.

world. The great fist of the sea gripped their diving machine in a 200,000-ton squeeze, but Piccard's father had built well, and the steel walls held. Finally, at 35,800 feet, the bathyscaph touched bottom. Then the two men leaned toward each other and slowly and solemnly shook hands, thus celebrating man's arrival at one of the last frontiers of the planet earth.

III : *The Sky*

THE DESIRE TO be airborne has probably existed since pre-historic man first watched the rhythmic flight of a bird. The fulfillment of this dream took nearly two million years to achieve.

One of the earliest expressions of man's wish to explore the atmosphere can be found in the ancient Greek legend of Icarus. He flew so high that the sun melted the wax by which his wings were fastened and he plunged into the sea. But this was fantasy, not fact, and the fate of Icarus was clearly intended to warn man against imitating the gods or creatures of the air.

The yearning to fly undoubtedly persisted, but it was nearly 2,000 years before any sort of scientific approach was employed. The notebooks of Leonardo da Vinci, a brilliant artist and engineer of the Renaissance, contain numerous drawings of mechanical devices designed to permit man to soar above the earth. Man's imagination, however, was again far in advance of his technology.

It was not until 1785 that man actually did get off the ground for a sustained period of time. A Frenchman named Jean François Pilâtre de Rozier had the distinction of being the first to do so—in a basket held aloft by a huge balloon.

Orville and Wilbur Wright pioneered the flying machine.

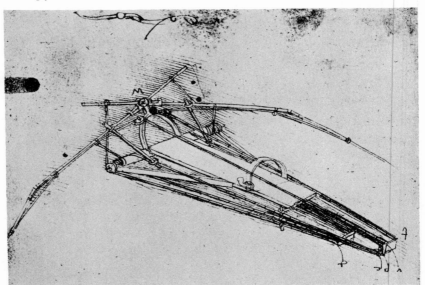

Drawing from the notebooks of Leonardo da Vinci

Leonardo da Vinci envisioned a simple platform with movable projections
simulating the wings of a bird that would enable man to fly.

The first test flight in 1903 was piloted by Orville, who
managed to stay in the air for 12 seconds.

Now man is rocketing through space and anticipating a trip
to the moon. He has opened a limitless frontier and, in exploring it, has already learned much about the air around and
the sky above.

Aurora Borealis: The Northern Lights

A ghostly light often dances over the northern rim of the
world, illuminating the night sky with brilliant flashes of red,
green, blue, and white. It is the aurora borealis, more com-
monly called the northern lights.

In the Far North, the aurora borealis is visible about nine
clear nights out of ten. Once a month or so, when conditions
are just right, the great blaze of light can be seen as far away

as New York City or Portland, Oregon. And perhaps once a year it is visible as far south as New Orleans or even Mexico.

Ancient peoples invented romantic myths about the northern lights. To the Vikings, for instance, they were a sign of the Valkyries riding through the sky. The Valkyries were thought to be blonde warrior goddesses who escorted the souls of dead heroes to a heaven called Valhalla, and the northern lights were believed to be reflections from the great golden shields the goddesses carried.

Today we know that the lights are produced by nuclear explosions on the sun. The explosions create clouds of atomic particles that spin around the earth, forming the Van Allen radiation belts. Later, as the particles cool, some of them leak out of the belts and fall toward earth, being drawn toward the polar region by magnetic attraction. As this solar fallout collides with earth's atmosphere, a form of atomic energy is released, producing the awesome spectacles of cosmic fireworks in the sky.

The aurora borealis can be seen only if the sky is dark. But it takes place both night and day, and it can be heard even when it cannot be seen. The static on radio and television is often caused by the solar storms that produce the lights.

The Jet Streams: Rivers of Wind

High in the sky, some 5 to 15 miles up, are roaring rivers of wind called the jet streams. They race almost constantly around the globe at speeds often reaching 250 miles an hour or more.

These air currents are of great size, sometimes a hundred miles wide and two to five miles deep. They usually flow west to east, one of them crossing the United States in a twisting, looping, ever-changing path. Other streams follow tropic

and Arctic routes; one circles above the globe at the Arctic
Circle.

The cause of jet streams is not fully understood. One theory
is that the big winds result from air-pressure changes when
masses of hot air mingle with cold. It is known that the jet
streams change directions with changing meteorological conditions and that the center of a stream is always 10 to 15 degrees warmer than the air on the northern edge.

The existence of such winds was discovered by accident
during World War II, when high-flying B-29 pilots encountered something odd in the skies over Japan. They found
at times that their planes seemed to hang in the air, making
almost no progress, though the engines labored mightily.
What had happened, of course, was that they had wandered
into the path of a jet stream and had tried to fly against it.

Today scout planes keep track of jet streams, and airliners
take advantage of them by riding along on streams blowing
in the direction of a plane's destination. The result is not only
a fast ride but a smooth one; the swift rush of the wind seems
to iron out all the up-and-down air movement that causes
bumpy flights.

The Van Allen Radiation Belts:
Barriers in Space

Far out in space are deadly invisible clouds that circle the
earth. They are called the Van Allen radiation belts and
were named for space scientist James A. Van Allen, who first
discovered their existence.

The Van Allen belts are made up of countless millions of
tiny atomic particles called electrons and protons. These
particles are fragments of "hot atoms," and they give off
searing radioactive rays.

The particles are spewed out by nuclear explosions on the
sun. As they hurtle through space, they are drawn into the

earth's orbit and so form immense clouds or belts that swirl endlessly around our planet.

Two such belts are thought to exist. Scientists believe that the inner belt circles the earth at the equator, taking the shape of a slightly flattened inner tube, and that it begins about 500 miles up, forms a layer 2,000 miles thick, and is about 1,000 miles wide. The outer belt is apparently a much more uneven circle, starting about 2,000 miles up and extending from 8,000 to 12,000 miles out into space.

The radiation belts present no danger to earth, for our atmosphere serves as a shield against the fatal rays. To obtain more specific knowledge of their close-range effects, however, scientists have been studying the information gathered by unmanned satellites equipped with geiger counters and other radiation-measuring devices. Engineers are using these data to perfect spacecraft that will provide man with the necessary protection against harmful radiation as he rockets through the Van Allen belts toward the moon and other planets.

One scientist has compared the radiation belts to invisible reefs in the vast sea of space. As with ocean reefs, the danger is at least partially conquered by the knowledge that they are there.

The Atmosphere: Shield Against the Sun

Enveloping the earth is a blanket of atmospheric gases that may extend as far as 600 miles into space. It is a protective blanket that warms us, shields us, gives us life.

The atmosphere, of course, provides the very air we breathe. There is, however, a good deal more to it than that. It is also a source of water, the gases of oxygen and hydrogen combining in the air to pour down as rain.

It fulfills another vital function by storing and distributing the heat received from the sun. Otherwise we would scorch in sunlight and freeze in shade.

The atmosphere serves also as an effective shelter against cosmic bombardment. It absorbs the sun's most searing rays, protecting us against radiation. And it provides friction that burns up invading meteors, turning them into harmless shooting stars. Without the atmospheric shield, earth would probably be hit by some 14 million meteors a day.

The blue of the sky, the white fluffs of clouds, and the rosy glow of sunset are all atmospheric effects, produced by the bending and scattering of light rays as they pass through the filter of air. If there were no atmosphere, daylight and darkness would appear suddenly, almost as though an unshaded lamp were being switched on and off in a room.

Sound is another atmospheric effect, occurring when air waves are set into motion. In airless outer space, meteors can collide and explode in fiery cataclysms that produce not a whisper of sound.

Approximately 99 per cent of the atmosphere is made up of nitrogen and oxygen, the rest being composed of eight other gases, which play important roles even though they appear in very small proportion. These eight gases are argon, carbon dioxide, neon, krypton, helium, hydrogen, xenon, and ozone, in that order of concentration.

These gases, which seem to be almost weightless, are present in such volume that they press against the earth with remarkable force. The pressure at sea level averages about 14½ pounds per square inch, which means that the average human being is constantly subject to a total air weight of about 18 tons. But we do not feel it any more than fishes feel the pressure of the ocean deep—and for the same reason; like the fish, man is equipped with internal pressure devices that provide a balancing force.

The balance of atmospheric and body pressure could be compared to two 18-ton weights propped up against either side of a very thin carboard partition. So long as the weights are equal, the partition is under no strain, but any increase or decrease in either weight would destroy the frail barrier. So it is with our bodies. If we should ascend very high in the sky, we would swell up and explode from unbalanced pressure within ourselves. Fortunately, the problem is solved easily enough by taking our atmosphere with us in pressurized cabins or space suits.

About 90 per cent of the weight of the atmosphere is concentrated in the troposphere, the bottom layer that extends about 5 to 10 miles from the earth's surface. Above it is a boundary layer called the tropopause, and above that is the stratosphere, where the gases become ever thinner, until they merge into the emptiness of space.

One very important atmospheric layer is the ionosphere, a belt about 200 miles thick, which begins about 50 miles up. It is an electrified region that transmits radio signals and very probably exerts great influence on earth's climate. It is also a very hot layer in the strata of generally cold gases surrounding the earth.

The most remarkable fact about our atmosphere is that it exists at all. Among all the planets in the solar system, ours may well be the only one that is wrapped in air. In most cases, in fact, it is known that the others are not. The only likely exception appears to be Mars, which may have a thin atmosphere—and, not surprisingly, it is also apparently the only other planet on which some form of life might possibly exist. It is thought that the changing colors on Mars could indicate a form of vegetation that comes and goes with the seasons.

Halley's Comet: Blazing Signpost in the Sky

A little more than half a century ago, Halley's comet flamed across the sky, creating immense excitement all over the world. Today this same comet is very far out in space, but it has wheeled around and is streaking toward us again. If it is on schedule, it should pay its next visit in 1986.

Land, Sea, and Sky

Halley's comet follows an elliptical course that is shaped rather like the outlines of a fat cigar. It comes from the direction of the sun, passes between the earth and the sun, then turns back toward the sun. It travels at about 40,000 miles an hour, yet it takes 76 years to complete one of its vast loops through space—a distance of six billion miles.

There are many comets in our solar system, but Halley's is by far the largest known. The flaming ball that forms its head is estimated to be 150,000 miles in diameter, the head alone being four hundred times the size of earth, with an enormous tail that streams out for millions of miles. Like the stars, it consists principally of a mixture of blazing gases.

The comet is named for Edmund Halley, a British astronomer who observed its passing in 1682. That, however, was not the first time that it was seen by man. As Halley himself discovered by checking old reports, the comet had often been noted before. It flashed through the heavens when Caesar died, when Attila the Hun was defeated, and when William the Conqueror became lord of England.

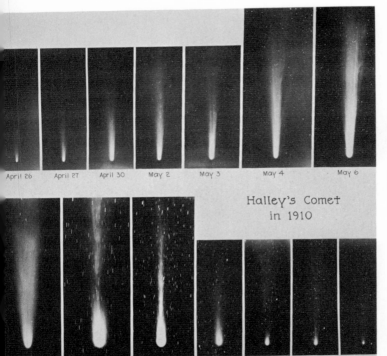

April 26 April 27 April 30 May 2 May 3 May 4 May 6

Halley's Comet
in 1910

Fourteen views of Halley's Comet as it appeared between April 26 and June 11, 1910.

Mount Wilson and Palomar Observatories

The comet, of course, had nothing to do with human history. However, the legend grew that its coming was associated with great and often fearful events. People thought of it as a sign that warned of terrible things to come. Thus its last appearance, in 1910, set off something close to world panic. Many thought that it would strike the earth, bringing the end of the world. Others believed that the earth would be smothered by poisonous gases that trailed in the comet's wake. And so when astronomers predicted that the great comet was approaching, people reacted in various ways. Some hid in caves. Some gathered in the streets to pray. And some watched from the rooftops, thinking that if this was the end, they wanted to see it coming.

After all that excitement, the comet itself proved to be something of a letdown. It was visible for about three months, but it proved to be not at all fearsome. At its brightest, it looked like a huge chalk mark drawn across the sky. As for hitting the earth, it did not come close. There is, after all, a lot of space between earth and sun. The last time it circled, the comet missed us by 60 million miles!

The Sun: Nuclear Furnace

The sun is 93 million miles from earth. This is a fortunate distance—near enough to yield heat and light, but not so close as to burn our small planet to a cinder.

The sun's power is almost inconceivable. It is thirty thousand times the size of earth, and its whole flaming, gaseous mass is one vast nuclear furnace. It burns itself up at the rate of four million tons a second, producing every second an explosion of energy equal to 10 billion H-bombs.

The process begins at the sun's core, where atoms of hydrogen are fused together under cosmic conditions of heat and pressure. The fusion releases a burst of energy that batters its way to the surface, erupting there in fiery explosions of heat, light, and radiation. Such eruptions, occurring continuously all over the surface, make up the normal "climate" of the sun.

Sun storms are more spectacular still. Scientists have been able to photograph such events in recent years, and the pictures are awe-inspiring. One sees flaming jets of gas shoot up 100,000 miles or more. Bridges of fire that could span a dozen earths suddenly form and as suddenly collapse. Sometimes a fountain of fire appears high above the sun and pours down a cascade of sparks. During such eruptions, large areas of the sun may shine with hundreds of times the normal brilliance.

Most of the solar energy is discharged into the vast void of space—quite wasted from the earthman's point of view—and the tiny fraction that is directed toward our planet is heavily filtered by the screen of our atmosphere. Even so, the energy received here is equal to a one-kilowatt electric heater on every square yard of the earth's surface.

From this energy we get much more than just warmth. It is very nearly the stuff of life itself. For in some still-mysterious fashion, sunshine is transformed by plants into the substances that produce growth and provide food for the world. The process is called photosynthesis, and scientists are constantly experimenting to determine how this takes place. If man could harness this power, a ray of sunshine might be turned directly into food, and the problem of hunger could be solved forever. The idea seems fantastic until one remembers that we have already unlocked the solar secret of nuclear fission. Photosynthesis could possibly be next.

The Moon: Window to the Universe

Sometime soon a bold pioneer will leave the first human footprint on the moon. If he lands at night, he may look up and see the strange sight of a full earth shining with the sun's reflected light. And if it is day, he will see all around him something stranger still—the eerie landscape of the moon itself.

Through the use of high-powered telescopic cameras and, most recently, a satellite equipped with television cameras, scientists have learned much about the appearance of the moon. Its landscape is formed of jagged rock piled high in mountains and scooped out in giant fissures and craters. It seems, in fact, a whole world of Mount Everests and Grand Canyons, but infinitely more stark and barren.

The craters are perhaps the most startling feature. There are some 30,000 of these great lunar pits, each of them forming a nearly perfect circle and each surrounded by a mountainous ridge. Some of the craters are four miles deep and are large enough to engulf Connecticut or New Hampshire. Whether large or small, they all resemble bomb craters, and they were probably formed by a relentless cosmic bombardment. It is thought that a great rain of meteors hurtled out of space, blasting the moon's surface repeatedly with explosions of enormous intensity.

The Ranger spacecraft, equipped with multiple television cameras, transmitted valuable data about the moon to scientists on earth.

Wide World Photos

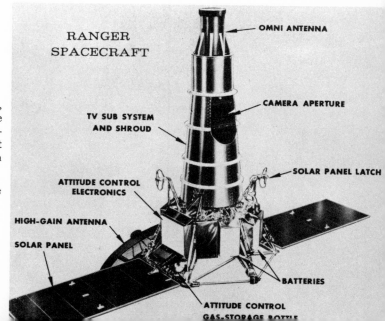

RANGER
SPACECRAFT

OMNI ANTENNA

CAMERA APERTURE

TV SUB SYSTEM
AND SHROUD

SOLAR PANEL LATCH

ATTITUDE CONTROL
ELECTRONICS

HIGH-GAIN ANTENNA

SOLAR PANEL

BATTERIES

ATTITUDE CONTROL
GAS-STORAGE BOTTLE

Such explosions could account also for the so-called lunar seas. These are smooth, dark areas to which early astronomers gave such poetic names as Sea of Serenity. Today we know that the moon contains no water and that a lunar sea must present a view about as serene as the bleakest stretches of Sahara or Death Valley. The now widely accepted theory is that the seas consist of hardened lava spewed out by the same explosions that gouged the craters.

Some scientists think that over millions of years, the lava may have crumbled into dust as a result of intense radiation from the sun. Such dust may be only a few inches thick, but it is possible that dust layers go down 50 to 60 feet. It is one of many questions that must be examined closely before a manned rocket can land safely on the moon.

Moon climate offers fearful hazards, too. There is almost no atmosphere, no air to store and distribute heat, with the result that the temperature soars and plummets. It is a blazing 220 degrees Fahrenheit by day, a freezing −243 by night. Even more dramatically, it changes by several hundred degrees in the few feet that separate the sunny and shadowed sides of a rock, the reason again being the lack of air to conduct the heat.

Why should man strive so hard to reach so uninviting an environment? One reason, of course, is the sheer challenge of it. We have climbed our highest mountains and plunged into our deepest seas; now we reach for the moon. There is also the motive of mental adventure. Certainly, firsthand investigation will reveal much more than any camera can capture and will add immensely to our knowledge of the universe in which we live.

Astronomers are especially anxious to use the moon as a platform for a giant telescope. It would enable them to see infinitely more than can be observed from earth. The reason has nothing to do with being farther out in space, for the few hundred thousand miles that separate earth and moon are of little consequence as cosmic distance is measured. The important difference is that earth is enveloped in an atmosphere; it acts as a kind of frosted glass, obscuring the light of sun and stars. Airless moon will provide a clear window to the universe.

The moon may provide us also with a look backward into the dim ages of earth's own past. It is thought that earth and moon were formed by the same process, the only difference being that the lighter moon lacked gravity enough to retain its atmospheric blanket. That in turn meant that it remained much as it was formed, with no development of water or soil, no growth or decay to clothe its naked rock. If that is true, then we may see in the moon a fossil earth that reveals much about our own planet's beginnings.

The Milky Way: Our Neighborhood in Space

We think of the Milky Way as being but one small streak in our sky, but actually it is all around us. It is our neighborhood in space.

This great galaxy is made up of more than 100 billion flaming suns, and it is spread over so vast an expanse of the universe that we record the statistics without really comprehending their meaning. Thus, distances are reckoned not in miles but in light years. Light travels at the speed of about six trillion miles a year, and it takes a ray of light 100,000 years to cross the Milky Way.

Astronomers believe that the galaxy is shaped like a huge three-armed spiral, a kind of celestial pinwheel that rotates through space. Our sun and its little collection of planets appear to be located about two-thirds of the way out from the center. We orbit around the rim of the flaming wheel approximately once every 220 million years.

Our position is such that we look south toward the center of the galaxy and north toward the outer edge; thus the southern skies afford far more brilliant star displays. In any sky, however, we see but a tiny fraction of the galaxy's stars, most of them being at distances so great that they can be observed only through telescopes.

Beyond the boundaries of the galaxy are still other star clusters—as large as or larger than the Milky Way. This fact was first suspected some 200 years ago. The proof was obtained about 40 years ago, when scientists built telescopes big enough to detect whole star systems in what had been seen previously as mere smudges of light far out in space. And then, very recently, the astronomers made still another discovery that staggers the imagination.

It had been thought that a few dozen galaxies might exist; but when the sky was examined inch by inch with telescopic cameras, it was found that star galaxies exist as abundantly as sand on the shore. If we mark off a little patch of sky—an area as big as the bowl of the Big Dipper, for example— and look out far enough through that one little keyhole in space, we can count more than 50,000 other galaxies like our own. And we have not seen to the end of it yet—if, indeed, there is an end.

The infinite number of stars has led to some fascinating speculations. It is known that earth draws life from its sun through a rare combination of circumstances that might occur only once in a billion times. These odds suddenly become very unimpressive, however, when one considers how many thousands of billions of suns are flaming in just one patch of sky that can be framed by two hands.

In short, it seems very possible that somewhere out there the rare conditions have occurred again, producing the mysterious phenomenon of conscious, intelligent life.

Some have declared it not only possible but almost certain.

So promising do the possibilities seem that scientists have built powerful radio receivers, tuning them to the vast reaches of the universe in the hope that some intelligent creatures might be trying to establish contact through radio signals. No trace of such signals has been heard as yet. But, then, as cosmic time is measured, it is only an instant ago that we began to listen for a sound that may have flashed many times through the void.

IV : *Elemental Forces*

THE ANCIENT GREEKS believed that the universe was composed of four elements—earth, air, fire, and water.

Today, of course, we think of elements in atomic terms. But the four factors the Greeks cited are indeed basic. Often they combine to form elemental forces.

The force, for instance, of frozen water rushing down an earth slope in the fury of an avalanche. . . .

Or the force of wind and water rubbing together to produce fire in the sky. . . .

Or wind and water in another pattern, producing a hurricane. . . .

Or wind churning earth into the black blizzard of a dust storm. . . .

Here are glimpses of the awesome powers released when such forces are on the move.

Avalanche: Snow Thunder

In high mountain country, a sound like booming thunder is often heard on clear, cloudless winter days. Mountaineers know what it means and look up fearfully, not at the skies but at the mountain slopes. For this particular thunder is the sound that warns of avalanche.

An avalanche roars down a mountainside in the Himalayas, carrying tons of snow in its path.

An avalanche is a heavy mass of snow sliding down a steep slope. There are, however, many kinds of avalanches. They may move at 3 miles an hour or at 300. They may roar down a mountain cutting a destructive swath only 10 feet wide, or they may appear as huge, mile-wide waves of snow. Each type has its own special dangers and peculiar characteristics.

One of the most common types is called the wet slide. It happens in the spring as snow melts, freezes, and melts again, all the time becoming heavier with the packed-down weight of its own water content. When it becomes heavy enough, it begins to push itself down the slope. It moves slowly at first, sometimes just inching along with little lurches, until a final lurch starts its rapid descent. Then a great wave of snow rolls down the side of the mountain, moving faster than a man can run. When it comes to rest in the valley below, it often piles up 20 to 30 feet high. One Alpine village was completely buried under such a slide, the tip of the village church steeple being all that stood above the immense flood of snow that suddenly engulfed the town.

A slab slide starts faster and is even more dangerous. It

occurs when a big chunk of snow or ice falls off an over-hanging cliff, triggering masses of dry, powdery snow into sudden motion. These slides can move at express-train speed, acquiring such force that they sometimes roar across a small valley and hurl themselves a hundred yards or more up a mountain slope on the other side.

Swiftest and deadliest of all are the airborne slides. Actually, they are not snowslides at all but, rather, snow swirls. They start when strong winds whip down the mountain, kicking up swirling flurries. Wind force and falling force combine to create a howling fury, the snow rolling and tumbling down the incline at speeds up to 300 miles an hour. Such slides create explosive shock waves, a violent rush of air sometimes knocking down large trees 50 feet or so ahead of the slide itself. After the slide passes, there is another shock wave, this one a suction force strong enough to snatch a man off his feet.

The Alps are particularly subject to avalanches, with at least 10,000 occurring there every year. Most occur in uninhabited areas and cause little damage. But for those who live in the region, the danger of avalanche is a constant threat.

The little village of Blons in the Austrian Alps offers a particular example. It lies at the foot of slopes that produce heavy slides, and it has suffered repeated avalanche disasters for the past 500 years. The people, however, have never thought of moving away. After each new catastrophe, the survivors dig themselves out and rebuild on the same spot. They look on avalanches as fishing people look on storms at sea, regarding them as a part of life that must be endured.

Lightning: Electricity in the Sky

Early men ascribed lightning to angry gods. The Greeks thought it marked the passage of flaming spears thrown by Zeus, and some American Indians believed in a monstrous, supernatural thunderbird that cast lightning bolts by winking its eye. Today we know that it is a natural phenomenon, an effect produced by the friction of wind and water, but we are still awed and sometimes frightened by the spectacle of fire flashing through the sky.

It is a force of frightening power. Lightning is believed to produce heat as high as 27,000 degrees Fahrenheit, considerably hotter than the surface temperature of the sun. The electricity generated in a single ordinary flash has been estimated at 500 million kilowatts, or more than one-fourth of the total capacity of all the electric power plants in the United States.

The speed of its strike has been calculated at up to 22 million miles per hour. The exact speed is a question much debated by scientists, but in any case it is much too fast for the human eye to follow. What appears to us as a single bolt of lightning is actually some two dozen strokes flashing back and forth in the manner of a neon sign. The average stroke lasts about ten-millionths of a second.

An explanation of lightning requires an understanding of electricity, but the basic mechanisms are quite simple. In effect, nature produces lightning by rubbing wind and water together. The process begins when rain falls through a thundercloud. Updrafts in the cloud catch some of the drops and break them into fine mist, generating a tiny charge of static electricity each time a drop is broken. It is comparable to the fact that water falling over a dam produces a form of energy easily converted into hydroelectricity. In the storm cloud the water falls up, down, and sideways as it is buffeted by swirling winds, and the cloud in some way acts as its own generator, building up positive charges at the top of the cloud and negative charges at the bottom. When the two charges become strong enough, lightning flashes between to complete the circuit.

Several pioneer scientists suspected the connection between

lightning and electricity, but Benjamin Franklin was the first
to prove it, sending a kite aloft in a storm to catch an electric
spark from a bolt of lightning. Though Franklin did not
realize it, his experiment was a reckless one; men have been
killed trying to repeat it.

Lightning kills an average of one person a day in the
United States; it causes property damage of more than half a
million dollars a week, most of it as a result of fire. There are
no estimates on the world toll, but the figure must be immense.
It has struck somewhere in the world at least 6,000 times in
just the brief time that you have been reading about it here.

Often it expends its fiery energy in freak effects. It has
been known to burn jewelry off women without harming the
wearers. Once, at Grand Rapids, Michigan, it struck a furni-
ture factory, setting it afire, then seconds later dispatched
a second bolt to set off a fire-alarm box just down the street.
When it strikes trees, it sometimes turns the sap to a gas that

The fire resulting from a lightning bolt destroys a New Jersey farmer's
barn. As this picture was snapped, a second bolt flashed through the sky.

Wide World Photos

expands so rapidly that the tree blows itself apart. And in one puzzling but well-verified case, lightning struck a tree so hard that a nearby well instantly dried up.

Some scientists believe that the chance effect of a lightning strike many millions of years ago helped to produce the most dramatic and most significant event in the history of earth. The theory relates to the time when there was no life anywhere on land or sea. It is thought possible that a bolt of lightning struck the sea, discharging a powerful burst of energy into the rich chemical soup of the water and changing the structure of some chemical substance in a way that, for the first time, enabled it to reproduce itself. Experiments designed to test the validity of this theory are being conducted now by biochemists in every country. To date, however, no one has succeeded in reproducing life from inorganic matter.

Thunder: Sound Waves of Lightning

Thunder is the sound wave that lightning creates as it rips through the air.

The intense heat of lightning causes air to expand along its channel, setting up a shock wave as the expanding air pushes violently against surrounding layers of the atmosphere.

A rumble of thunder is produced by a long bolt of lightning at a considerable distance. The sound arrives in stages, so that it reaches our ears as a whole series of noises.

A sudden, sharp thunderclap occurs when a lightning bolt arcs directly overhead, sound waves from every point on the arc reaching us simultaneously. In effect, a thunderclap is lightning heard stereophonically.

A knowledge of thunder enables us to calculate the distance at which lightning is striking. The flash is seen almost instantaneously, while the sound wave travels along behind at the much slower rate of about 1,100 feet a second, the speed

varying slightly according to temperature and other atmospheric conditions. It is thus a simple matter to judge the
approximate distance by counting the seconds between flash
and bang.

Dust Storm: The Black Blizzard

A wind-driven swirl of dust seems a casual, harmless
phenomenon. But multiplied by many swirls, it becomes a
thing of fury that spreads ruin in its path.

Americans had their first experience with such disaster
during the Dust Bowl era of the 1930s. For five straight years,
dust storms called black blizzards rolled back and forth across
the Midwest, destroying crops, driving thousands of farmers
from their homes, sometimes suffocating men and beasts.

A witness to one of the big storms described it as a dense
black cloud of dust that rolled and tumbled over the prairie
at 60 miles an hour, the dust rising a thousand feet and
extending across the horizon for as far as the eye could see.
Where the dust settled, it filled ditches, blocked highways,
and piled up like snow in drifts five feet deep. In the eye of
the storm, daylight turned to darkness, and visibility for hours
afterward was cut to as little as 50 yards.

Another black blizzard raged all the way from Texas to
Illinois, stripping an estimated 350 million tons of topsoil from
the land and saturating the air with a dense pall of dust that
rose as high as 15,000 feet. The fallout was scattered over half
a nation, the storm obscuring the sun for five hours and more
over cities as widely separated as Chicago, Baltimore, and
New York.

Dust storms have appeared on every continent and in
almost every age. Some believe that such storms were at least
partly responsible for the decline of early civilizations in
China, Egypt, and Asia Minor. Today North Africa and the

Middle East are particular storm centers. The desert dust and sand are blown westward in such quantities at times that ship navigation is impeded off the coast of Africa.

Often man contributes to dust storms by careless plowing of the land, removing the protective cover of grass and trees. But dust-storm conditions are also created by nature. The most intense of all such storms came at the end of the last Ice Age, when retreating glaciers exposed huge globe-girdling belts of land stripped bare of all vegetation. Then dust storms raged for centuries, scouring the land down to bedrock or piling up dust deposits in thick layers called loess. The rich farm country of Iowa derives its fertility from loess extending as deep as 100 feet, while in China some loess deposits are 700 feet deep.

Hurricane: Great Wheel of Wind

A hurricane is a circular wind that spins across the ocean like a giant top, building up speed as it goes and churning the sea into tidal waves. In hurricane disasters the wind and waves usually combine to deliver a one-two punch of devastating power.

To be caught in a hurricane is an unforgettable experience. Hours before the storm strikes, its approach can be seen, felt, and even smelled; there is a quality in the air that is ominous yet exciting and strangely exhilarating. The sensations are not imagined. The breeze changes, becoming heavy, damp, and salty. The sea begins to change, too; a long, heavy surf rolls up the beach with the booming sound of muffled drums. A glance at the barometer shows that atmospheric pressure is dropping steadily as air is sucked away by the whirling motion of the approaching storm.

Then the hurricane hits. Shrieking with wind, black with rain, hurling terrible waves against the shore, it often rages for two hours or more. When it passes, there is a dead, flat calm, but that is only the moment of rest in the eye of the storm. The pause is followed by another assault as the second half of the big wheel-shaped storm passes overhead. The blow is similar to the first, but now the wind comes from the opposite direction.

Hurricane winds have a minimum velocity of 73 miles an hour and sometimes rise to more than 200 miles an hour. The waves driven by these winds have been known to thunder against the shore with literally earthshaking force. When a particularly violent hurricane devastated New England in 1938, the crashing surf caused tremors that were registered by earthquake instruments as far away as Alaska.

Hurricanes increase in speed and power as long as they

Dust storms in Texas covered fields and highways with drifts of sand, destroying the crops buried under the dust.

United Press International Photo

This diagram shows the pattern of wind circulation in a hurricane. The spiraling movement is caused by collisions of warm and cold air.

U.S. Department of Commerce, Weather Bureau

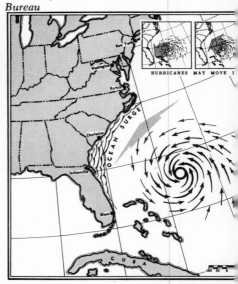

DIAGRAM OF WIND CIRCULATION IN A HURRI

move across water; they begin to diminish when they swirl inland. In the final lunge, however, they usually inflict their greatest damage by flooding low-lying coastal areas. The worst example in American experience occurred in 1900, when a hurricane swept over Galveston, Texas, killing 5,000 people and wrecking more than 3,500 homes. Another historic instance was a hurricane that roared across the Florida Keys in 1935, drowning 400 men who were at work on a road.

To prevent such disasters, the weather bureau now maintains a complex network of hurricane spotters. Meteorologists study the wind patterns, pinpointing places where the storms are likely to start. Radar specialists track the storms as they move over the sea, and pilots who call themselves hurricane hunters fly their planes right into the howling gales to gather other valuable information. Then ship and shore radios crackle with warnings, and black flags flutter over threatened communities; those in the path of the storm are thus given precious extra hours in which to seek shelter and prepare for the blow.

Hurricanes are created by collisions of warm and cold air, the weight difference in the two air masses causing a turbulent, spiraling movement. The spinning motion of earth provides an extra shove, starting an atmospheric whirlpool. Once started, it grows of its own accord, spinning faster and becoming ever larger as it pulls in more and more air.

A land cousin to the hurricane is the tornado or cyclone, known also as the twister. It originates from the same basic forces, but differences in atmospheric conditions result in some quite different effects. The tornado usually rides high in the sky, only now and then dipping down a twirling black finger to loose its fury against the earth. Usually, too, it has a storm front only a few hundred yards wide, whereas a hurricane may have a front as much as 500 miles wide. In its own way, however, the tornado can be even more dangerous.

The localized violence of a tornado can be seen in this short stretch of railroad track. The steel tracks were bent out of shape as a twister swirled across them.

Wide World Photos

Its winds sometimes reach 800 miles an hour—four times as fast as the hurricane and faster even than the speed of sound. It strikes with a vicious whipping motion that gives it added power.

As a tornado whirls around a house, it may create a vacuum that causes the house to blow itself apart from the sudden expansion of the air pocket within. Then again, it may wrench a house from its foundations, hurl it through the air, and set it down almost intact half a block away. Or still again, it may reach down ever so lightly, strip a row of shingles off the roof, and swirl away so quickly that people next door will not know it has passed. The odd, unpredictable power of the tornado was most notably illustrated by one twister that picked up a broomstraw and drove it deep into a wooden post, embedding it as neatly as though it were a nail driven in by a hammer.

V : *Hidden Wonders*

A FEW CENTURIES AGO the words "Dark Continent" often were used to indicate Africa on a map. It was the map maker's way of admitting that he just did not know what was there.

Today there is no place on earth that can lay fair claim to such a mysterious title. The tallest mountain and the deepest abyss have both been conquered; the poles, jungles, and deserts have all been discovered and pretty well explored. But there remain many fascinating opportunities for the adventurous sightseer.

A horseback ride through Utah mountains takes one to a place called Forbidden Canyon. This is one of the country's great scenic wonders, but because it cannot be reached by car, few have seen it.

Or one may go adventuring back in time by exploring the frozen graveyard of the woolly mammoths.

And there is always the sea, with its many secrets still to be uncovered.

Rainbow Bridge: The Secret of
Forbidden Canyon

Utah's Rainbow Bridge is an immense stone span that leads from "nowhere to nowhere." It is one of the nation's least

U.S. *Department of the Interior*
National Park Service Photo

The scenic wonder of Rainbow Bridge is the result of wind and water erosion. This natural bridge spans approximately 278 feet and arches to a height of more than 300 feet.

known scenic wonders because it is hidden away in a place so remote that only a few have been privileged to see it.

The bridge is a result of erosion, the forces of wind and water carving away at a huge slab of stone for thousands of centuries. This natural bridge is at once massive and graceful, spanning about 278 feet in a vaulting arch that rises to 309 feet—high enough so that a football field could be upended beneath it with room to spare. The roadway at the top is 33 feet wide and more than 40 feet thick. Yet the structure is so symmetrical, so perfectly proportioned that it looks as though it were designed by an artist.

The bridge is located in Forbidden Canyon, a few miles from the point where the Colorado River crosses the Utah-Arizona border. The surrounding countryside is a rugged, almost uninhabited jumble of mountains and canyons, and so the existence of the bridge was not discovered by white men until the twentieth century. The Indians knew of it, however, and they spread tales of "the rock that goes over." In 1908 a Paiute Indian guided the first white visitors to the scene.

Today Rainbow Bridge is set aside as a national monument, but it remains almost as wild and lonely a place as when it was found. It can be reached in only two ways. One can go by boat along the Colorado River to the mouth of Forbidden Canyon and then hike the last six miles to the bridge. Or one can reach it with a long day's horseback ride from Navajo Mountain Trading Post. It is a tough trip either way, and Rainbow Bridge receives only one rare and determined visitor for every 10,000 who go to see the Grand Canyon.

Graveyard of the Mammoths: Nature's Deepfreeze

It was once a common belief that old elephants went to a certain place in the jungle to die. For centuries, men searched for this elephant graveyard, but no one found it or discovered whether it ever existed. There is, however, a section of the world that might well be called the graveyard of the mammoths.

The mammoth graveyard is spread over a vast area of Alaska and Siberia in the region of the Arctic Circle. It is an area that has been described also as "nature's deepfreeze." Here, preserved in the eternal ice, are the frozen bodies of giant mammoths and other prehistoric creatures.

The story of this graveyard is best illustrated by one of the classic discoveries. In 1900 a native was traveling through northern Siberia. The barking of his dog attracted him to a place where a landslide had ripped away a slab of earth. There, rising half out of the landslide, as though struggling to escape, was a woolly mammoth. The creature had perished thousands of years before, and yet its huge, shaggy-haired body was almost perfectly preserved. Its meat was still edible. Indeed, wolves had been tearing at the carcass, and the smell of the meat had attracted the dog.

Russian scientists excavated the animal for a museum. In doing so, they were able to reconstruct the story of its death. The mammoth's position was that of a creature attempting to climb out of a pit. It had a broken foreleg and a fractured hip, probably from a heavy fall. Very likely the fall set off a landslide that buried the beast at once. Obviously it was a sudden accident—half-chewed food was found in the mammoth's mouth. In the stomach were grasses with seeds on them, indicating that it happened during the brief Arctic summer or early fall. The winter that followed evidently laid down a thick protective mantle of snow and ice; the mammoth lay locked in the frozen earth until, ages later, another landslide exposed it to view.

Countless other mammoths must have met similar fates during the thousands of centuries in which the great beasts roamed the Arctic country. Many of the remains are no doubt preserved. It takes luck to find them, for the country is but little explored, and the evidence might lie anywhere under the frozen tundra. Even so, scientists and explorers over the last half century have reported seeing more than three dozen mammoth carcasses, many of them virtually intact. One of the more recent finds in Alaska was the head, trunk, and one foreleg of a baby mammoth.

Occasionally, too, the tundra yields up the remains of other Ice Age creatures. An extinct musk-ox has been found almost entirely preserved. Bones and other remains have also been found for such now-vanished beasts as an Arctic camel, a huge horned bison, a big lion-like cat, a large wolf unlike any living today, and a bear even larger than the towering Alaskan brown bear.

So far the Arctic deposits have revealed only the faintest traces of man himself. We know, however, that primitive man , passed this way, hunting the other creatures and being hunted by them. Perhaps someday the tundra will yield the most sought-after evidence—a perfectly preserved specimen of our distant ancestor.

Nodules: Treasure on the Ocean Floor

Scattered over the ocean floor are lumps of dark, round metallic rock about the size and shape of cannonballs. They are called nodules, and they are potentially more valuable than all the sunken treasures of pirate gold.

Nodules contain rich quantities of copper, iron, nickel, cobalt, and manganese. They are so thickly clustered in some areas that oceanographers estimate their value at more than a million dollars for every square mile of ocean floor. For some unknown reason, they appear most abundantly in the Pacific, though some have been found in the Atlantic, too.

Apparently the nodules were created through precipitation of minerals that are always present in seawater. Excess minerals evidently dropped to the bottom and formed crusts around such objects as pebbles and sharks' teeth. The process has gone on for millions of years, storing up a treasure that will yield immense dividends once man has mastered the complex problems of mining the deep.

Atlantis: The Fabulous Lost Kingdom

For countless thousands of years, the sea has risen and fallen, sometimes receding to uncover great areas of land, sometimes surging back to bury large islands or even whole countries. Out of this age-old drama has come the story of Atlantis, a legendary kingdom that was supposedly engulfed by the sea.

The legend describes Atlantis as one of the first civilizations to be formed in ancient times. It was located, so the story goes, on a huge island off the west coast of Europe. It is said that the king of Atlantis lived in a palace of gold and silver and that his fighting men went forth in warships to conquer an empire larger than Caesar's. Then the sea rose in its awesome power, rolling over Atlantis and destroying it in a day.

The Greek writer Plato recorded the story of Atlantis some 2,300 years ago. He said that the existence of such a place was well known to the ancient Egyptians, but it is hard to tell whether he was reporting something he had heard or was merely spinning a tale. In any case, many men believed it, and some have searched ever since for the lost kingdom. Marine explorers have sailed back and forth over likely areas, using depth-sounding equipment to probe for places where an island might have sunk into the sea. They have even gone down in diving suits to prowl about on the ocean floor. But they have not found any trace of Atlantis.

Does this fabulous lost kingdom lie undiscovered somewhere beneath the waves? Probably not. Today almost all marine experts agree that Atlantis is only a myth. Many of them, however, believe that the story does illustrate something that happened repeatedly in human experience. The sea did rise time and again, swallowing up whole tribes of people who lived on low-lying islands or near the shores.

One of the best-known examples is the Dogger Bank, a famed fishing ground in the North Sea off the coast of England. Many thousands of years ago, this area was land covered by forests and inhabited by Stone Age men who hunted the mastodons and other prehistoric beasts. Then melting glaciers swelled the oceans, which engulfed the land. Now fishermen who work these waters often find arrowheads and bits of bone in their nets.

Flood disasters occurred often, and memories of them must have been preserved by the few who somehow survived. We can guess that the experiences were passed on from parents to children and that the stories kept growing as they were told around countless campfires. Perhaps that is the way the romantic story of Atlantis began.

VI : *American Landmarks*

Approximately 3,500 years ago, a seed fell on the slope of a mountain. It took root and grew, and it kept growing until it became the largest living thing on earth. It is still living today, a majestic tree in California's Sequoia National Park.

Long before the tree sprouted, another event left its mark on the landscape of this continent. A big glacier moved down from the north, slicing a riverbed in two. The glacier has vanished now, but the river rolls on. When it cascades into the old glacial trough, it roars and tumbles in the thunderous display that is Niagara Falls.

And long before the twin falls were formed—back even perhaps in the dim, distant time before life began—a river that no longer exists coursed through what is now Arizona. We can trace its history today in the magnificent spectacle of Grand Canyon.

Such are the natural history and wonders of the American landscape.

Niagara Falls: Twin Cataracts

The Niagara River is a calm stream, broad and beautiful, as it flows from its source in Lake Erie. But only a few miles farther along, it becomes a raging torrent, boiling and tumbling as it rushes along, thundering awesomely as it hurls itself over the great cataract of Niagara Falls.

The river is part of the border between the United States and Canada, and it splits around a spit of land called Goat Island just before it tumbles over the brink. As a result, there are two falls, known as the American and the Canadian. The American Falls is about 167 feet high, several feet higher than its rival, but otherwise the Canadian Falls offers much the better show. It is some 3,000 feet wide, about three times as broad as the other, and the pull of currents channels 95 per cent of the water to the Canadian side.

Together the two cataracts thunder down at a rate of some three and a half million gallons of water a second. And the spectacle has been going on for thousands of years—ever since a glacier cut across the river's course and scooped out the gorge into which it plunges.

The river has since done some giant-sized scooping of its own. Under the heavier Canadian Falls, there is a basin nearly 200 feet deep, carved out of solid rock by the continual hammering of the water. The rocky face of the falls is also being chewed away bit by bit. In the last 50,000 years, the cataract has moved seven miles upstream, tearing away its own cliff as it slowly retreats.

Niagara Falls is famed also for the effect its spectacle exerts on human emotions. The Indians who inhabited this region were moved to religious awe, hearing what they thought was the voice of the Great Spirit in the roar of the water. According to one legend, an Indian tribe sacrificed its most beautiful maiden to the falls every year, the girl being decked in flowers, then placed in a white birch canoe to ride down the fearful drop. There is a legend, too, that the practice was stopped after a grief-stricken chief threw himself into the falls to accompany his daughter in death.

In more recent times, people have gone over the falls in the spirit of daredevil adventure. The first was a forty-two-year-old widow named Annie Taylor, who took the ride in a home-made barrel, hoping that the stunt would make her rich and famous. She took a dreadful beating but, luckily, survived. Since then, at least six others have tried it, only half of them surviving. Still others have tried to swim the churning caldron beneath the falls, but a French stunt man named Blondin topped them all when he pranced high above the falls on a tightwire.

Such stunts are prohibited now, but the natural splendor of Niagara Falls continues to attract thousands of visitors each year.

The Everglades: Historic Hideout

Spreading over the southern tip of Florida is a lush, almost tropical swamp called the Everglades. It covers some 3,500

An aerial view of some of the low-lying islands that dot the waters of the Everglades.

U.S. Department of the Interior
National Park Service Photo
by M. Woodbridge Williams

square miles and is one of the last great wildernesses still to be found in the United States.

The Everglades is often portrayed as a dense jungle rising out of a stagnant marsh. Actually, it contains as much prairie as jungle and is not stagnant at all. In fact, it might well be described as a broad, shallow, sluggish river dotted with innumerable low-lying islands.

The "river" begins as an overflow from huge Lake Okeechobee in southern Florida. Water spills out of the lake and spreads over a broad basin that forms the swamp. It is 50 to 80 miles wide and winds along for about 100 miles until it reaches the sea. The slope of the land is very gentle, about three inches to the mile, and so usually the water seeps rather than flows. But heavy rains can bring a flood of water rolling across the swamp, submerging the low-lying land and changing quiet channels into surging streams.

The upper half of the swamp is prairie country, covered with brown, sharp-edged sawgrass that grows higher than a man's head. The Indians called this region River of Grass.

The lower half is a dark, tangled jungle interlaced with twisting streams. Even experienced guides have been known to lose their way in this section of the Everglades. It is so wild and desolate that for a long time it served as a hideout for desperate men.

The first people to find refuge in the Everglades were Indians driven from their lands by the advance of white civilization. Remnants of several tribes fled into the swamp, formed a new Indian nation called Seminole, and there resisted for many years all efforts of the American Army to dislodge them. A small group was never conquered, and descendants of those Indians still live in the swamp, yet maintaining a proud independence.

For a long period the swamp was also a haven for outlaws. As late as the 1920s it was traditional that strangers who met in the Everglades did not ask one another's names.

Today much of the Everglades is set aside as a national park, providing a place of refuge not for men but for wild creatures. The swamp's alligators, for instance, were once hunted almost to extinction, thousands of them being slaughtered for their hides. Now they are protected by law. Rare birds such as the graceful snowy egret have found safety in the swamp, too.

One of the most notable of the swamp's wild creatures is the American eagle. It once roamed the skies across the length and breadth of the land. Now the Everglades provides one of its last remaining nesting grounds. Oddly, eagles have survived in greatest number in two very different climates—in the steaming heat of the Everglades and in the frozen wastelands of Alaska.

The Mississippi River: Father of Waters

The Mississippi takes its name from the Indian words *misi sipi*, meaning "big river." It has been known also by many other names, all of them suggesting its power and majesty. To some Indian tribes it was Father of Waters, and to some it was Old Big Strong; later, the Negro slaves called it Old Man River.

By any name, the Mississippi is indeed a mighty river. It begins in Minnesota, and at its source it is only a little brook, so narrow that an agile boy can jump across it. But it winds along for more than 2,300 miles, gathering to itself the waters from thousands of other streams, until it swells in some places to a width of three miles. At the Gulf of Mexico, where it flows into the sea, it pours out some 724 billion cubic yards of water a year. That is 8 times as much as Germany's greatest river, the Rhine, and 177 times as much as England's Thames.

The Mississippi's drainage area covers 31 states and a part of Canada, a vast area of more than a million square miles.

United Press International Photo

When the Mississippi River overflowed its banks in 1937, entire towns along its shore were flooded.

Most of the streams between the Appalachians and the Rockies eventually mingle their waters in the Mississippi.

It is an unpredictable river. It has often changed course, sometimes cutting a new channel for itself almost overnight. In the process, it has left former river towns stranded inland and has flooded other towns that stood in the way of its new channel. Greenville, Mississippi, Delta, Louisiana, and Arkansas City, Arkansas, are some of the towns from which the big river receded. Prentiss, Mississippi, Napoleon, Arkansas, and Kaskaskia, Illinois, were engulfed when it changed directions.

Sometimes, too, the river surges over its banks to inundate whole areas. In the great flood of 1937, the Mississippi spread out in some places to a width of 80 miles, driving 700,000 people from their homes and causing nearly fifty million dollars' worth of damage. Such disastrous floods are not likely now—vast systems of dams and levees have been built to tame the river—but people who live along the Mississippi's banks still watch with wary eye when swift, churning waters begin to rise.

An American writer named Samuel Clemens once described the Mississippi as "the crookedest river" in the world. He spoke from experience, for in his early days he had piloted the big, handsome paddle boats that plied up and down the river. When Clemens became a writer, he signed his stories Mark Twain, taking the name from a call that rivermen used as a navigation signal.

Through the centuries the Mississippi has added much flavor to the nation's history and folklore. Part of that flavor is preserved in the names of river cities like St. Louis and New Orleans—names that remind us that French explorers discovered the Mississippi and established its first settlements.

At a later stage the Mississippi marked a frontier toward which pioneers moved. Still later it was a great trade route, the riverboats accounting for almost half the nation's cargo haulage in the days before the railroad appeared. During the Civil War, a Union drive to choke off the South's riverboat traffic resulted in the bloody battle of Vicksburg.

Today only a few of the old paddle boats live on, a colorful reminder of the river's past. But a new river fleet has appeared, towboats and barges that haul millions of tons of cargo along the waterway every year. As is said in a famous song, "That ole man river, he just keeps rollin' along."

The Marching Dunes: Michigan's Little Sahara

Along the eastern shores of Lake Michigan are great sand dunes that move restlessly back and forth. The rate of movement is slight, only a foot or so a month at the most, and the results are not noticeable to the casual observer. But over the

The marching dunes along the eastern shore of Lake Michigan move imperceptibly but relentlessly, burying anything in their path.

months and years, such dune movements have buried trees, buildings, even whole villages.

A pioneer settlement called Newburyport was the first to be overwhelmed by the slow, relentless movement of sand. The settlers fought against it for a while, trying to fence the dunes off, but eventually they gave up and abandoned their town. Later, the same fate overtook a town called Singapore, located near the mouth of Michigan's Kalamazoo River. Occasionally a dune shifts to reveal a chimney or wall of buried Singapore.

The marching dunes are found in some 20 places along the shore, covering several thousand acres in all. They result from peculiar weather conditions, winds and tides piling up sand so fast that vegetation fails to cover it. The wind shapes the sand into huge drifts, and new sand is continually added, until the dunes become top-heavy and begin to slide. For a long time, Michigan's "Little Sahara" was regarded as wasteland. Today it is a park area valued for its wild beauty.

Great Salt Lake: Legacy of the Ice Age

Great Salt Lake in Utah is about eight times as salty as the sea. Some odd things happen as a result.

Salt water is much more buoyant than fresh, and so it is almost impossible for a swimmer to sink in this peculiar lake. There is, however, a disadvantage. In Great Salt Lake, one floats like a cork, with the lightest end up, and the lightest end of the human body happens to be the feet. Swimmers must work constantly to keep the feet down and the head up, but they can float easily and naturally if they tie small weights to the feet.

Sea gulls, pelicans, and other aquatic birds that live in the area encounter a special problem of another sort. When they swim on the lake, their wing feathers sometimes become so encrusted with salt that they are unable to fly.

The water in Great Salt Lake is 20 per cent heavier than ordinary water because of the salt content. Every gallon of the water contains roughly a half pound of salt.

In winter, some of the salt is squeezed out in the process of freezing. Then one finds solid bars of almost pure sodium sulfate piled up in the shallows. As for the beaches, they are white, glistening salt beds packed four feet deep.

An explanation of Great Salt Lake requires an understanding of the process called erosion. Each drop of rain that falls dissolves a little of earth's chemicals, including an infinitesimal speck of salt. Some of this salt is mixed back into the earth as rain evaporates, but much of it is carried away in streams and dumped into the sea. By this process, over countless millions of years, the sea acquired its briny character.

At Great Salt Lake the same process took place in a much more concentrated form. It began at the end of the last Ice Age, when melting glaciers covered most of western Utah with a vast layer of water 1,000 feet deep. The lake then contained nearly twenty thousand times as much water as it does now, and the contour of the land was such that most of the water could not drain into the sea. It became an almost stagnant lake, slowly drying up through thousands of years of hot, dry weather. As the water evaporated, the natural salt content was left behind to saturate what remained of the lake.

There is a frontier legend that trapper Jim Bridger was the first to discover the lake. In any case, he camped on its banks and reported that he preserved his meat for the winter by soaking it in the salt water for a day. Today commercial companies make use of the salt on a large scale, extracting about 90,000 tons of it a year. That is not enough to make any notable difference, as there are still some six and a half billion tons of salt in the water.

The Great Salt Lake area is also famous as the place where the Mormons established their colony after they fled from persecution a century ago. The Mormons transformed the surrounding desert into a prosperous settlement, but not without a terrible struggle. One year when a horde of insects threatened to destroy the crops, the settlement was saved by flights of sea gulls that came shrieking from the lake to devour the pests. In Salt Lake City, there is a statue of a sea gull to commemorate the event.

Carlsbad Caverns: Nature's Underworld

One of the world's biggest cave complexes is New Mexico's Carlsbad Caverns. It is more than 1,000 feet deep at its lowest point, and it winds through the earth for some 23 miles.

The cave passages spread out in places to form enormous underground vaults. The most impressive is a T-shaped chamber called the Big Room. It measures nearly 2,000 feet along the main stem of the T and is famed for the great dome of its ceiling, which arches to a height of 285 feet. The world's tallest tree could stand easily in Carlsbad's Big Room.

Stalactites, stalagmites, and other rock formations stud the caves, taking weird and often beautiful shapes. Some glow with soft, translucent colors; others are ghostly white. They were formed by water that seeped into the caves, depositing limestone on walls, ceilings, and floors.

The limestone yields a clue to how the caves were formed. The process began about 200 million years ago, when this area was a shallow sea. Tiny marine animals swarmed thickly, depositing skeletons to form a great limestone reef. Much later the earth heaved and buckled, tilting the reef, splintering it with countless cracks and fissures. Then rainwater poured over the tilted surface for thousands of centuries; the water drained into the cracks and ate away at the soft limestone to carve out Carlsbad Caverns.

Indians knew about the caves in prehistoric times. They left campfire traces around an entrance shaft, but apparently they never entered the cavern. It must have seemed too dark and deep, too mysterious and dangerous. It is quite possible, in fact, that no human being set foot in the caves until almost a century ago.

A twelve-year-old ranch boy named Rolth Sublett claimed the honor of being the first. He said that in 1883 his father lowered him into a shaft at the end of a long rope. Later, an

Stalactites, stalagmites, and other rock formations create a strangely beautiful landscape in the underground world of Carlsbad Caverns.

United Press International Photo

Old Faithful spews out 10,000 to 15,000 gallons of water once every 65 minutes. The geyser is a favorite attraction at Yellowstone National Park.

Courtesy of the American Museum of Natural History

adventurous cowboy named Jim White explored the caves, using kerosene torches to light his way through the long miles of dark passages.

Stairways, ramps, and elevators now make a descent into Carlsbad easy. The visitors, however, see only three miles of the caves. Beyond the last tourist point, there remains the primordial underworld of Carlsbad's depths. Here bats make their summer home, blind mice creep about, and curious insects record their presence with the merest whisper of sound in the dark. There are about 25 species of animal life in the cave, half of them found nowhere else on earth.

Old Faithful: Clockwork Geyser

There is a rumble in the earth, a great hiss of steam, and then a tremendous roar as a column of scalding water bursts out of the ground and shoots high into the air. Such is the eruption of Old Faithful at Yellowstone National Park.

Old Faithful is famous, of course, for the almost clock-like regularity of its eruption. It occurs faithfully, as the name suggests, every 65 minutes. Now and then it may go off schedule by a minute or two, but seldom by more than that.

It is also known for the sheer power of its magnificent display. It spews out 10,000 to 15,000 gallons of water at a time, creating a white-hot plume of steam that soars as high as 150 feet. The eruption lasts four minutes, and it looks and sounds like one long-drawn-out explosion.

The geyser has been erupting at the same rate and on the same schedule for as long as records of its action have existed. The average rhythm of eruption has changed by only one second in the last 80 years. And in that period, Old Faithful has pumped out some seven billion gallons of water.

Yellowstone National Park contains more than a hundred other geysers, many of them spectacular sights. Castle Geyser shakes the ground when it erupts, the explosion often lasting a half hour and more. Another, known as the Giantess, throws up a jet of steam 250 feet high. And still another, the Grotto Geyser, is famed for the weird, twisted patterns of its steaming plumes.

The park also contains thousands of hot springs. The difference is that a spring bubbles, while a geyser blows. Sometimes a spring turns into a geyser. One hot pool is called Chinaman's Spring because, supposedly, many years ago a Chinese laundryman used it for washing clothes. According to a park legend, he dropped a bar of soap into the spring and triggered a geyser that sent him scampering and blew his pile of clothes 40 feet into the air.

Park attendants keep strict watch to prevent visitors from dropping objects into a hot spring, since they may set off a dangerous eruption.

Both the hot springs and the geysers are caused by deep earth scars that run through the park. These scars, or faults, expose red-hot layers of rock far down in the earth's crust. Water seeps into the faults, comes into contact with the rock, and is heated to the boiling point. Usually, the water merely bubbles up to form a hot spring. In some cases, however, the size and shape of the fault line make it act like a plugged-up teakettle, preventing the boiling water from escaping. Then pressure builds up to a geyser eruption.

Yellowstone's strange geysers were discovered more than 150 years ago by a trapper named John Colter. No one believed the things he described, and people laughed off his account as a frontiersman's tall tale. Today, however, the geysers are famous all over the world, and as many as a million people come to view them every year.

The Grand Canyon: Great Ladder of Life

The most awesome abyss on earth is the Grand Canyon, in northwest Arizona.

Size alone makes the Grand Canyon a magnificent spectacle. It is nearly a mile deep, is 217 miles long, and ranges from 4 to 18 miles in width. It is famed also for its rugged beauty and for the fascinating facts it reveals about the geologic history of our planet.

The canyon began as a riverbed about one and a half billion years ago, at a time when the earth was almost barren and lifeless as the face of the moon. The planet then had no covering of dirt, only bare rock. But there was rain, probably a great deal more rain than falls now. For millions of years the torrents of rainwater poured over the bare, rocky hills, cutting out a deep channel that became the canyon.

The water erosion continues today as the silt-laden Colorado River tumbles through the ancient stream bed at the bottom of the canyon. On an average day, about 500,000 tons of sand, gravel, and rock are swept through the gorge by the surging river. Inhabitants of the area say of the river water that it is "too thick to drink, too thin to plow."

River action alone, however, was not enough to carve out this enormous scar in the earth. When our planet was still being formed, upheavals of unimaginable force thrust up high-walled cliffs on either side of the riverbed. Then, over the ages, avalanches tore away great sections of the cliffs, widening the canyon to its present dimensions.

All this and more is written on the canyon's steep and rocky walls. At the very bottom of the Inner Gorge, the first chapter of the story is etched in the dark rocks that covered all the earth when the Grand Canyon first began to take shape. In these rocks, there is not a single fossil to hint that life existed when the canyon began.

A little higher on the walls, life leaves its first record in the fossil imprints of small green scum-like plants called algae. They flourished at a time when this whole region was covered by a primordial sea. Preserved in the same layers of rock are ripple marks left by that long-vanished sea.

U.S. Department of the Interior
National Park Service Photo

A view of the Inner Gorge of Grand Canyon, seen from Bright Angel Trail.

As one continues up the slope, the record continues, so that the canyon walls come to seem like a great ladder of life. There are remains of extinct, very primitive sea creatures that resembled horseshoe crabs. Higher up are the once-muddy but now rock-frozen tracks left by some of the first creatures that came out of the sea to live on land. And still higher, the fossilized remains of creatures that first took to the air can be found.

In places along the canyon wall, erosion and earth upheaval have blurred the record, so that a chapter of earth's history is lost. Geologists call this gap the "great unconformity." One can place a fingertip across a line that marks several million missing years.

Man has left few impressions on the Grand Canyon; but, then, man has been only a brief and recent visitor as time is measured in this vast abyss. If the entire earth story represented in the Grand Canyon were compressed into a 24-hour movie, the part dealing with man's existence would occupy only the last 58 seconds. And the four centuries since explorers discovered the canyon would be cut down to the merest flick of an eyelash, one-fortieth of a second.

The Grand Canyon gives us not only a cross section of time, but also a richly varied sample of life conditions in our own age. Between the top of the canyon's highest rim and the bottom of its deepest gorge, one finds six of the world's seven climates, or life zones, from polar to equatorial; only the tropic zone is missing. It can be snowing at one level of the canyon, raining below, and dry as a desert still farther down.

The mere existence of the canyon as a physical barrier has changed the nature of animal life. Thus, on both sides of the canyon, there is a type of squirrel with tufted ears and a chestnut-striped back. But the squirrels on the north rim have white tails and black belly markings, while those on the south rim are gray-tailed and white-bellied. They have been separated by the huge gorge for so many thousands of years that they have developed into different species. The two sides of the canyon yield similar differences in species and subspecies among such creatures as porcupines, rabbits, gophers, coyotes, and rattlesnakes.

Tourists who go into the canyon learn for themselves what an immense barrier it is. At Grand Canyon National Park, one can make the descent by riding a mule down steep and twisting Bright Angel Trail. The trail in many places skirts within a foot or two of cliffsides that drop away for half a mile or more. Sometimes, too, the mules lean out over the edge to pluck at shrubbery growing from the cliffs. The sure-footed beasts have never lost a rider yet, but many a visitor has been frightened half to death before completing the descent into this greatest canyon.

Death Valley: Hottest, Driest, Lowest

Crossing the Funeral Mountains, the traveler comes to a high ledge called Dante's View and looks down to see Death

Valley below. It is a stark and desolate scene, the most forbidding desert in North America.

Death Valley extends over nearly 3,000 square miles; most of it is in California, but one edge laps over the Nevada border. It is the nation's hottest and driest region. The summer temperature rises to a blistering 134 degrees Fahrenheit in the shade, and the rainfall is less than one and a half inches a year.

It is also the site of the lowest altitude in the Western Hemisphere. The exact spot is marked by a briny, foul-smelling pool called Badwater, which seeps out of the desert floor at a point 282 feet below sea level.

The desert landscape is one of jagged rock, glistening salt beds, and shifting sand dunes. For all its desolation, however, there is a wild grandeur to the place. Especially striking are the massive rock formations, carved by erosion into eerie shapes and painted by nature in bold splashes of red, white, black, purple, green, and gold. One unexpected formation is an extinct waterfall that towers 50 feet high at the edge of the desert. Its face is scoured by grooves the size of railway tunnels, marking the channels down which a mighty river foamed and tumbled in another, very different age.

A bird's-eye view of the fabulous desert castle built by Walter Scott, better known as Death Valley Scotty.

United Press International Photo

Badwater, in Death Valley, is 282 feet below sea level—the lowest altitude in the Western Hemisphere.

United Press International Photo

More surprising still is the presence of a fishpond in Death Valley. It is at Saratoga Springs, an alkaline pool about 20 miles from Badwater. It is thought that fish were stranded here during glacial floods, the descendants gradually adapting themselves as centuries of changing climate squeezed them into the last refuge of a small, hot, almost stagnant pool. The same tenacious struggle for life is seen in the more than 500 types of vegetation that appear in the desert. Some, such as the gnarled mesquite and greasewood trees, send roots down as deep as 60 feet in quest of moisture. And there are plants that grow not in soil but in salt; they have become so adapted to Death Valley conditions that they would die if transplanted to fertile, well-watered earth.

Man, too, has learned how to survive in this harsh wasteland. The earliest inhabitants were Indians, who drifted around the rim of the desert, existing on the sparse plant growths and enjoying a rare feast when they caught a lizard. Later, a party of California gold rushers became the first white men to enter the area. They suffered terrible hardships while crossing Death Valley and gave the place its grim name. Still later, other pioneers came to mine the desert salt beds, hauling the salt away in wagons drawn by 20-mule teams.

The most famous inhabitant was Walter Scott, better known as Death Valley Scotty, who claimed that he had found a rich vein of gold somewhere in the area. People still argue about whether the gold mine existed or not, but it is certain that Scott had some secret source of wealth. He built a fabulous desert castle, which is still standing in Death Valley today.

Death Valley is now a national park, equipped with many facilities to ease the hardship of a desert crossing. It remains, however, a place that should be approached with caution. Road signs warn that cars break down easily in the scorching heat, and tourists are constantly reminded to take along ample supplies of water.

La Brea Asphalt Pits: Storehouse of Skeletons

Hancock Park, a Los Angeles city park, is studded with pits in which smooth black asphalt wells up from the ground. If one scoops out some of the asphalt, the hole soon fills again as new asphalt oozes up.

The pits are called La Brea, from a Spanish term meaning "tar." They are also known as the Death Pits because so many animals sank into the sticky asphalt in ages past.

The skeletons of saber-toothed tigers, mammoths, mastodons, giant sloths, midget horses, and other prehistoric beasts have been found in the La Brea pits.

The pits began millions of years ago as underground pockets of oil. Then some great upheaval split the earth open, exposing the oil to the surface. Sun and rain filtered away the oil's lighter elements, leaving the pits filled with tarry sludge. For centuries afterward, the pits were deathtraps, sucking down the beasts that blundered into them, sometimes snaring even the light-footed birds that lit on the surface. Today, however, the asphalt has become quite firm—about as hard as frozen butter. One can walk on it and suffer no more damage than tar-stained shoes.

The pits were discovered in 1769 but remained just a curiosity until a man named Hancock began to dig out the asphalt in 1875. In 1906 the digging turned up the first great animal find, the bones of a saber-toothed tiger. These, of course, were the remains of an extinct animal, a huge beast with teeth almost a foot long curling out of its mouth. The diggers must have marveled at the discovery; but after examining the skeleton, they tossed it aside and went on with their work. In the next 30 years, countless other skeletons were dug out and thrown away by men interested only in obtaining asphalt.

Eventually, scientists realized that the pits contained a wonderful record of animal life in prehistoric America. The pit owner gave the property to the county of Los Angeles, and museum experts took charge of the digging. Fortunately, the pits continued to yield bones by the hundreds—enough to piece together a remarkable picture of the strange beasts that roamed the land long ago.

San Andreas Fault: Mother of Earthquakes

Running almost the entire length of California is a mammoth flaw in the earth's crust. It is called the San Andreas Fault and is known also as the Mother of Earthquakes.

A fault line is an unhealed scar in earth's tough outer skin. In the case of the San Andreas Fault, the scar is more than

A section of the San Andreas Fault, a scar in the earth's surface that runs from the Gulf of California to a point north of San Francisco.

United Press International Photo

700 miles long. It begins somewhere in the Gulf of California, cuts across Northern Mexico, then slices up through California, finally disappearing into the sea at a point north of San Francisco.

Layers of dirt have sifted over the fault line, and vegetation has covered it, so that one might walk across it and not know it is there. But under the thin covering, there is a great slash in the earth that may be as much as 50 miles deep.

This earth wound was torn open millions of years ago, at a time when the planet was rocked with terrible convulsions. Some scientists think the convulsions came from within, as a result of fiery gases expanding in the earth's interior. Others hold an almost opposite theory, believing that the planet was squeezed violently when the outer crust cooled and contracted. In any case, it was a cataclysmic force that thrust up mountains, carved out valleys, and reshaped entire continents.

Some lesser but still powerful force yet wrenches the planet today, creating a continual strain. Along the San Andreas Fault, this force tugs the earth's crust in opposite directions, pulling northward on one side of the fault and southward on the other. The strain builds up until the old scar is torn open again. Then a sound like thunder rumbles out of the earth as the ground above heaves and trembles with the force of earthquake.

Earthquakes triggered by the San Andreas Fault have claimed more than 1,000 lives and destroyed nearly two billion dollars' worth of property. Among those disasters was the famous earthquake that leveled San Francisco in 1906. The shocks that occurred then were so powerful that two mountains on either side of the city were moved 10 feet farther apart.

Some other San Andreas earthquakes have produced results that were merely curious. In pioneer days, one such quake tore a rancher's corral in two, dragging half of it in one direction and half in another; when the shock subsided, the once round corral had been reshaped in the pattern of a big S. In modern times, another convulsion along the fault line created a small but puzzling international problem—it moved a section of the United States–Mexican border almost 10 feet.

The Largest Trees: Kings of the Forest

Standing like tall sentinels on the slopes of the Sierra Nevada Mountains are the lordly sequoia trees. They are the largest living things on earth.

Some of the sequoias are more than 200 feet tall. Two dozen immense groves of them are found in California's Sequoia and Kings Canyon National Parks.

The giant of them all is a tree called the General Sherman. It measures 36 feet in diameter at the base—a trunk as wide as a city street—and rises a majestic 272 feet in the air. It weighs an estimated 2,000 tons and contains enough wood to build 40 five-room houses. Its bright cinnamon-colored bark is two feet thick. Everything else about it is on a similar heroic scale.

To some, the tree's age is even more impressive than its size. It sprouted about 3,500 years ago, at a time when the pharaohs ruled ancient Egypt. It was living and growing through almost the entire period of Western civilization. It still puts forth fresh seed every year.

Some others in the sequoia groves are nearly as old, nearly as big. The next largest, the General Grant, is 20 feet thick at the base and 271 feet tall. Another sequoia landmark is the hollow log of a long-dead tree called the Fallen Monarch. The cavity is so huge that it has been used to stable horses.

Still another is called the Room Tree. A devastating forest fire burned a room-sized hole in its base and left charred openings that look very much like a window and door. But the tree is so tough that it healed its wounds; today new bark is slowly enclosing the terrible scar.

Sequoias rank as the largest trees because of their combined height and girth. They are not the tallest, however. That honor goes to the redwoods that grow along the coast of California and Oregon. They are 10 to 15 feet thick at the base and soar up as high as 367 feet. They, too, are ancient, the patriarch among them being about 1,500 years old.

Not surprisingly, the sequoias and redwoods are members of the same tree family. The type appeared during the Mesozoic era, more than a hundred million years ago, and spread at one time over most of the Northern Hemisphere. Then the glaciers came down from the north, leveling everything in their path. Sequoias and redwoods survived only in a few isolated places that the glaciers failed to reach.

When the glaciers retreated, the great trees stood unmolested for centuries. The Indians were awed by them, believing them to be associated with powerful spirits; the braves walked in silence when they passed through sequoia forests. Then the white man came, and the silence gave way to sounds of saw and ax. Thousands of the fine old trees were chopped down for lumber, and it seemed for a time that all of them would be destroyed. Fortunately, Congress stepped in, setting aside a few sequoia and redwood groves as national parks. Thus the largest trees still stand, attracting millions of park visitors who come to marvel at their size and grandeur.